Forewo

By Deborah, Duchess of Devonshire

Beautiful, mysterious, fragile and unique to Derbyshire is Blue John. No two pieces of this curious mineral are alike. The colours, in bands, range from purple and dark blue to yellow, buff and off-white, and their disposition is always different.

The strange attraction of this Derbyshire spar has been recognised for hundreds of years. In the eighteenth century it was made into bowls, vases and goblets, while artist/craftsmen such as Matthew Boulton set pieces in ormolu mounts making them highly desirable examples of the decorative arts which are now prized by collectors all over the world.

You can visit the old mines at Castleton and see a fairyland world of weird formations of stalactites and stalagmites and get an idea of the risks taken by the explorers who discovered this intriguing mineral centuries ago.

Whether you visit the mines or see Blue John made into an enviable piece of jewellery your curiosity is aroused. Now it can be satisfied because no one is better qualified to write about Derbyshire's most interesting mineral than Trevor Ford. This scholarly book will be welcomed by all who want to learn about Blue John and it is with great pleasure that I commend it to you.

Above: The Grapes Table made by William Woodruff

Below: A series of slices of Blue John dovetailed to make a pseudo-nodule

Opposite: An unusual Blue John vase fitted with ten Blue John bells hanging from the rim

Derbyshire Blue John

Trevor D. Ford

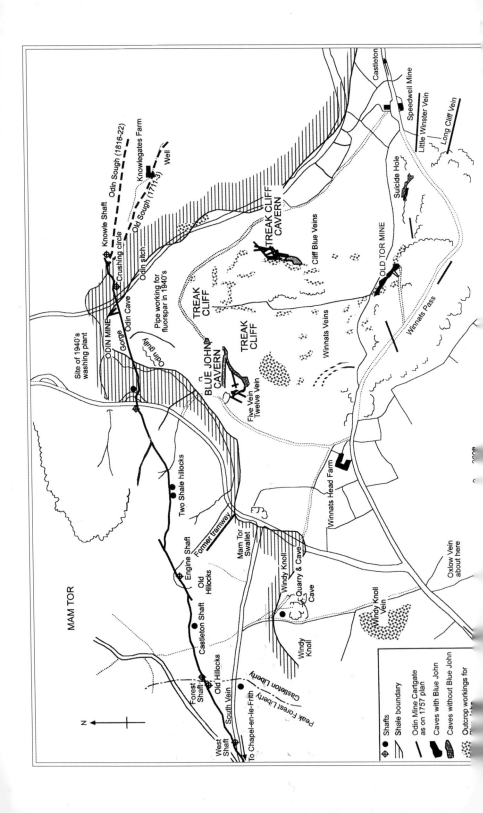

CONTENTS

Blue John is a variety of the common mineral fluorspar. Composed of calcium fluoride (CaF_2), fluorspar can be almost any colour of the rainbow, with white, cream or yellow translucent varieties being the most common. Fluorspar got its name at least as early as the 15th century from its property of improving the fluidity of slag in smelting operations. The variety Blue John is characterized by bluish purple and white banding. Mined around Castleton in North Derbyshire it has been used as a semi-precious ornamental stone for more than two centuries.

As with all fluorspar varieties, Blue John crystallizes in the cubic system, with surfaces made of a mesh of interpenetrating cubes. The colour bands show sections across cubic crystal growth layers giving a zig-zag effect. Articles made of Blue John show these alternating stripes of blue to purple and white or yellow and give it its attractive appearance whether it be large vases or small jewellery stones.

Blue John has long been regarded as uniquely present only in the caverns of Treak Cliff at Castleton, though similar varieties of fluorspar are known in small quantities elsewhere in the Peak District and at a scatter of localities around the world. These look-alikes will be discussed again later in this book.

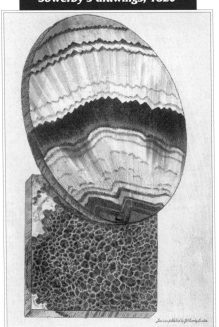

Sowerby's drawings, 1820

Understanding the nature of Blue John necessitates a thorough look at its geological surroundings and the following chapters discuss the origin of the unique stone. The details of its crystal structure have been revealed by scientific investigations as described in the mineralogy chapter.

Methods of extraction from the mines and caverns take up a further chapter as does the preparation and manufacture into ornaments and jewellery. The history of its discovery and early use is partly based on incomplete documentary evidence and partly on unsupported tourist guide books but it is a fascinating story nevertheless. Finally, a brief review is presented of some notable collections.

There are several stories about the origin of the name Blue John. The name does not appear in archives until about 1766 when Lady Mazarine was recorded as leasing "ye mine of Blue John". Robert Adam was incorporating Blue John in his fireplace designs in 1760 but it was not recorded under that name then. Matthew Boulton called it Blew John in a letter dated 1768. Before that it was referred to as either "Derbyshire Drop" or "Derbyshire Spar", though the latter at least has been used for other minerals such as alabaster. It was also known as "Radix Amethysti" though it is unknown how this misleading pseudo-Latin term arose. Another Latin name was "Fluor Spatosus" though this generally meant any fluorspar, not just Blue John.

There are two basic stories as to how the name Blue John arose. Firstly, there is the tale that it was a corruption of the French description of its colour "bleu et jaune", meaning blue-and-yellow. This is logical but there is little evidence to support the story. Blue John is reputed to have been used by the French ormolu manufacturers in the same way as Matthew Boulton did in Birmingham, but this argument is based on the style and technique of the ormolu being French and no archival record of Blue John being exported to France is known. Enquiries in France about ormolu with Blue John articles in their stately chateaux have drawn a blank. It seems much more likely that the French gilt fittings were imported into Britain and added to Blue John here, either by Matthew Boulton or by other craftsmen.

The second alleged origin for the name Blue John is that the lead miners mistook Blue John in the dim candle-light undergound for the zinc mineral sphalerite which they knew as Black Jack, and when they discovered their mistake they amended the name. In other words their Black Jack was really Blue John. This tale is thought unlikely to be true by those who know the Derbyshire lead mines well: the miners were too observant to make such a mistake. It is much more likely that they knew there were two similar minerals and they simply gave them similar names.

Another story has been accredited to John Kirk who is said to have invented the name when he "discovered" what we now know as the Blue John Cavern in 1770, but the name was already in use before the alleged discovery. So this story can be discounted.

In short, whilst the French connection is sensible and logical, no evidence to prove it has come to light. The confusion of Black Jack with Blue John can be ignored, but an origin in miners giving two similar minerals comparable names is possible. Perhaps future archival research will uncover more evidence.

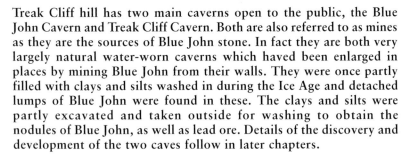

Treak Cliff hill has two main caverns open to the public, the Blue John Cavern and Treak Cliff Cavern. Both are also referred to as mines as they are the sources of Blue John stone. In fact they are both very largely natural water-worn caverns which haved been enlarged in places by mining Blue John from their walls. They were once partly filled with clays and silts washed in during the Ice Age and detached lumps of Blue John were found in these. The clays and silts were partly excavated and taken outside for washing to obtain the nodules of Blue John, as well as lead ore. Details of the discovery and development of the two caves follow in later chapters.

On the north-north-west side of the hill, close to the western margin of the Mam Tor landslip, the **Blue John Cavern** was partly mined as early as 1709 under the name Waterhull. Whilst a few tourists were taken down in the 1770s they had to negotiate a miners' wooden ladder down The Pothole and it was not until 1836 that a proper route was developed by blasting out an improved descent and laying flagstones for paths. Today's visitors go down some 30 steps at the entrance into the so-called Roman workings, mainly late 18th century workings for the Twelve and Five Veins. Descending The Pothole by a zig-zag stairway, visitors reach the level Ladies Walk. A branch passage high on the right leads into the Bull Beef workings. Soon afterwards, the visitor reaches the Grand Crystallized Cavern, the first part of the main series of high water-worn caverns. A low opening on the left leads into the Organ Room, named from a row of stalactite columns later smashed by vandals. The Organ Room vein of Blue John occurs here.

Descending the main series of caverns the visitor passes a narrow slot on the left leading down into the Old and New Dining Room Vein workings. Beyond this, visitors enter the large Lord Mulgrave's Dining Room. Lord Mulgrave is said to have spent three days exploring the caverns in 1843 and he and his party of miners stopped here to eat their meals (nothing is known of how Lord Mulgrave came to be exploring the cavern).

A branch passage which now houses the Mirror Pool leads back into the Dining Room workings, with fine Blue John. A small patch of this variety is in the cavern wall nearby. Not part of the tourist route, the Dining Room workings extend to New Cavern, with its own vein of Blue John. A climb nearby leads through Stemple Cavern to the Fairy Grotto. Two high chimneys near here were once the miners' entrances to this part of the cave system. From Lord Mulgrave's Dining Room the tourist route descends to the vast Variegated Cavern where the tour ends. In spite of various claims of caverns going for several miles beyond the barrier, in fact the series only extends for a few hundred metres before closing down to an impenetrable sump. A branch passage, the Inferior

Gallery, leads back towards the Fairy Grotto. Visitors then have the delight of climbing 175 steps back to the surface.

Treak Cliff Cavern lies part way up the steep eastern face of Treak Cliff and is reached by steps and path from the road. It comprises two series of caverns. The Old Series is the combined Cliffside and Miller Mine workings dating from the 18th century. The New Series is the row of beautifully decorated stalactite caverns found during spar-mining operations in 1926 and opened to the public in 1935. Visitors enter through a low tunnel, partly in the shales, which is probably the adit recorded as George Whittingham's Level in 1784, and really much older. A dispute at this time resulted from the miners from the two mines breaking into each others' workings. From the end of this adit visitors climb through a series of caverns with several veins of Blue John with the Cliff Blue pattern of colouring. Many of these veins fill voids in the boulder bed, noted in the geological account below. A short branch from the Fossil Cavern leads to part of the Millers Vein workings, where stone traditionally used for knife handles was obtained (see section on veins below). Climbing the long flight of steps visitors enter the Witches Cave. Many patches of both Cliff Blue and Millers Veins occur in pockets here and there is a small area with stone similar to the Five Vein high up in one corner. Voids lined with Blue John often have "dog-tooth" calcite crystals in their centres. Workings continue uphill above the tourist route

with further veins of Cliff Blue and with patches of hatterel (see below) and occasional rosettes of baryte crystals. These high workings once linked with the open quarries on the hillside. Descending a few steps below the Witches Cave, visitors enter the stalactite caverns opened to the public in 1935. These include Aladdin's Cave, Fairyland, the Dream Cave and the Dome of St Pauls, all with abundant stalactites and stalagmites, but no Blue John. A return to the surface is made through an adit driven during the 1920's spar mining operations.

There are other mines on Treak Cliff. High on the north side of the Winnats Pass the crags contain small veins of Blue John. These were followed downwards to the west-north-west and became the Old Tor Mine. Worked intermittently from the 18th century onwards it is now closed for safety reasons by order of H.M. Inspector of Mines. Another mine in these crags lay directly above the western end of the Old Tor Mine but its entrance has been filled in. Other workings for Blue John were on the flat top of Treak Cliff; near Odin Mine at the foot of the northern slopes of Treak Cliff; and near Windy Knoll, but there is little visible of these veins today. Odin Mine itself was worked for nearly a mile westwards beneath the shales of Mam Tor but is not known to have produced any Blue John. A branch vein within Odin Mine was the Blue Cap Vein, but the reason for this name is unknown and it is not accessible today.

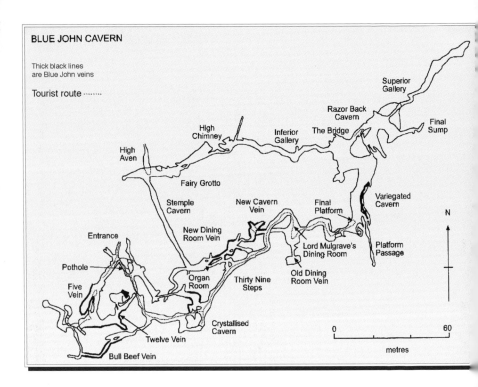

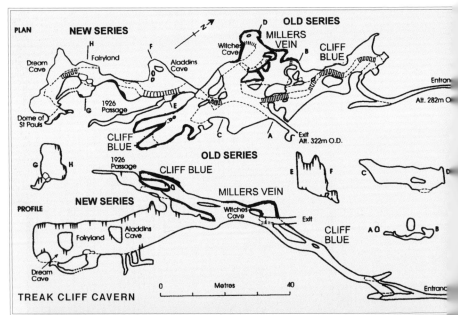

Top: The Blue John Cavern and below: Treak Cliff Cavern,
showing the positions of the Blue John veins

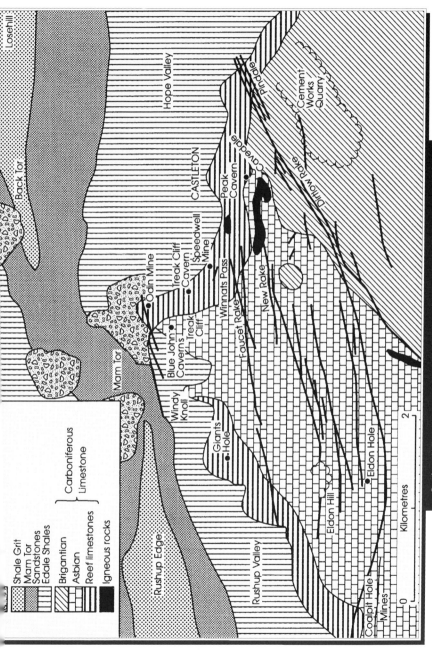

A simplified geological map of Treak Cliff and its surroundings

Legend:
- Shale Grit
- Mam Tor Sandstones
- Edale Shales
- Brigantian
- Asbian — } Carboniferous Limestone
- Reef limestones
- Igneous rocks

Labels on map: Losehill, Back Tor, Hope Valley, Mam Tor, Rushup Edge, Rushup Valley, Windy Knoll, Blue John Caverns, Odin Mine, Treak Cliff, Treak Cliff Cavern, CASTLETON, Speedwell Mine, Peak Cavern, Cement Works Quarry, Pindale, Cavedale, Dirtlow Rake, New Rake, Faucet Rake, Winnats Pass, Giants Hole, Eldon Hill, Eldon Hole, Coalpit Hole, Mines

Scale: Kilometres 0 1 2

Treak Cliff is the most northerly point of the Carboniferous Limestone massif of the Peak District. A roughly triangular limestone hill, it is flanked on the northwest and east by shales which can be seen in the landslip scar of Mam Tor. The shales constitute the lowest part of the Millstone Grit group of rocks. Mainly composed of sheets of sandstone interlayered with shales, the Millstone Grit forms the high moors and escarpments of Kinderscout, Stanage Edge and Millstone Edge which surround the White Peak.

The southern margin of the Treak Cliff hill is formed by the Winnats Pass, a deep gorge cut into the limestone. Mineral deposits, including those of Odin Mine and of Blue John, lie within the limestone, which is also the host rock of cave systems open to tourists. Both the limestones and the Millstone Grit were formed in the Carboniferous period of geological time, and for a full understanding it is best to take things in chronological order as summarized in the accompanying chart.

The Carboniferous period of geological time lasted for 64 million years from 354 to 290 million years ago. The limestones of the Peak District massif date from around the middle of that period, with those of Treak Cliff being about 320 million years old, formed in a subdivision of Carboniferous time known as the Asbian Stage. The limestones are largely composed of the fossilized remains of millions of sea creatures, broken up to form lime-sand with the grains later cemented together to form rock. Some limestones, however, were lime-mud bound together by the action of microscopic algae – these are the "reef limestones" usually known as

mud-mounds today. The formation of the limestones took place in tropical seas when Britain lay astride the Equator: Britain has been drifting slowly northwards ever since and is now more than halfway to the North Pole!

In the geography of Carboniferous times, most of the limestones of Treak Cliff represent a group of reefs along the northern margin of a lagoon occupying much of the Peak District. The main part of the reef now forms the crest of Treak Cliff, with flat-lying lagoonal limestones to the southwest extending across the upper parts of the Winnats Pass and far away to the south. The reefs had a steep outward slope and this is now seen as the steeply sloping fore-reef slope of the east face of Treak Cliff. It overlooks what would have been a deep water basin in Carboniferous times and the contemporary deep sea deposits are hidden beneath Hope Valley floor. To the west of Treak Cliff, beyond Windy Knoll, the limestones form another cluster of reefs but this time facing west or northwest and partly hidden beneath the shales on the south side of Rushup Edge. Together the reefs of Treak Cliff and Windy Knoll border a flat-topped dome.

The shales and Millstone Grit sandstones covered it all giving us a structure which later trapped fluids moving through the rocks.

Some 5 to 10 million years later, from the end of Brigantian times (i.e. the end of the Carboniferous limestone age) into the beginning of the Millstone Grit period (known to geologists as the Namurian subdivision of Carboniferous times) the Treak Cliff dome was raised up above sea level and subjected to erosion. An eroded limestone surface generally known as karst developed, broadly comparable with eroded limestone landscapes named after the "krs" limestone terrain of Croatia, with a shallow ravine along the line of the Winnats Pass and a scatter of small caves. The topmost layers of limestone were removed by erosion before the shales arrived and parts of the highest limestone beds were broken into boulders which rolled or slid down the outer reef slopes to form a boulder bed lying on the limestone slopes of Treak Cliff.

A million or so years later Treak Cliff sank beneath the waves again and it was progressively buried beneath a vast sheet of sediments which accumulated for over 10 million years of Namurian times. These sediments are collectively called the Millstone Grit Series. They came from a series of deltas at the mouth of a major river draining an ancient mountain range of which the Scottish Highlands are the remnants. The sediments include spreads of coarse sandstone, known as gritstone, separated by layers of shale. Together gritstones and shales totalled about 1500 metres in thickness so that the limestone was buried to that depth in the Earth's crust.

Towards the end of Namurian (Millstone Grit) times, say around 300 million years ago, the South Pennines were depressed even further beneath the swamps, lakes, rivers and smaller deltas of the Coal Measures. These buried the limestones and their Millstone Grit cover to an even greater depth adding a further 1500m to the thickness of the cover so that by the end of Carboniferous times 290 million years ago the limestones were at a depth of 3 kilometres. Such a burial of course raised the temperature by roughly 1°C for every 30m depth so that the limestones were at temperatures of at least 100°C. The depth of burial also increased pressures by several kilobars.

The above story sets a scenario for the process of mineralization, i.e. the introduction of mineral fluids into the limestone massif with the resulting formation of mineral veins. The first aspect of this process is related to the development of the geological structure, that is the updoming of the whole South Pennine area, which occurred as part of major Earth movements at the end of the Carboniferous period. The up-doming meant a change from the subsiding basin to form the Pennine anticline. The up-doming also resulted in the progressive removal of the former cover of Coal Measures and at least part of the Millstone Grit by eroding the top off the upfold, so gradually bringing the limestones back towards the surface with a lowering of temperatures and pressures. The stresses and strains of these changes also caused major fractures in the Earth's crust and these are seen in the Peak District as the larger mineral veins known as rakes. Odin Rake at the foot of Mam Tor is a good example where the strata broke along a roughly east-west line over a mile long, yielding a fissure system ready to be filled with minerals.

Deep burial of sediments results in chemical changes to the materials of which they are composed. Certain elements are released into the pore waters to yield fluids rich in ions which then migrate to sites suitable for chemical reaction. The ions released include chlorine, fluorine, sulphate, calcium, barium, lead and zinc, as well as minor traces of uranium. Chemical reactions between these ions gave us the minerals found in the many veins: more will

be said about them in the chapter on Mineralogy.

The chemical reactions which change sediment into rock also involve the remains of micro-organisms which have rotted to varying degree whilst buried. In short, such reactions are part of the organic-chemical system which produces hydrocarbons, the fore-runners of oil and gas. These too accumulated in the up-domed structure of Treak Cliff and relics of the oils are now to be seen as the bitumens oozing from the rock at Windy Knoll.

So, over some 20 million years around the end of the Carboniferous period geologists visualize the genesis of a hot fluid containing both the inorganic ions such as chlorine, fluorine and sulphur as well as the hydrocarbons dispersed within the deeply buried sediments. As temperatures and

View of Treak Cliff & Mam Tor from the east

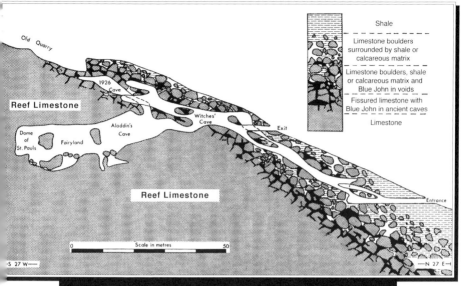

Shale

Limestone boulders surrounded by shale or calcareous matrix

Limestone boulders, shale or calcareous matrix and Blue John in voids

Fissured limestone with Blue John in ancient caves

Limestone

Profile through Treak Cliff Cavern showing the cave & mine workings in relation to the reef limestone, boulder bed & the overlying shales

pressures increased by burial towards the end of the Carboniferous period and later reduced by uplift and erosion, the fluids migrated out of the shales into the limestones to meet both percolating rain water and trapped sea water. The result is a sort of chemical soup where complex reactions took place and precipitated the minerals seen in the vein systems of the Peak District today. The hydrocarbons acted as catalysts and were later oxidized so that they were lost into the atmosphere, but relics can be seen oozing from the limestone at Windy Knoll. Blebs of bitumen also occur inside many fossil shells.

The chemical reactions thus took place in an environment of changing stresses and structures in late Carboniferous and early Permian times, say 300 to 280 million years ago. The changing stresses meant that the fluids migrated towards the regions of least pressure, i.e. the uplifting South Pennines. Both the fissures and the ancient cave systems were ready for the minerals to be deposited in them. In short, the ions were mainly generated within the deeply buried limestone basins flanking the Pennines and the hydrothermal fluids moved into the relatively higher Derbyshire Dome to form the mineral deposits found today.

The 280 million years since the Derbyshire Dome and its mineral deposits were formed have seen further changes, but they have

Chronological Chart

Periods	Millions Of Years	Main events of Geological Time before present
Quaternary	1 - 2	*Great Ice age (Pleistocene)*
Tertiary	2 - 65	*Uplift and erosion*
Cretaceous	65 - 142	
Jurassic	142 - 206	*Burial beneath strata subsequently eroded*
Triassic	206 - 248	
Permian	248 - 290	*temporary uplift end of Carboniferous - folding, faulting, mineralization*
Carboniferous (upper)	290 - 310	*Coal Measures swamps and Millstone Grit deltas middle of Carboniferous - uplift of limestone massif*
Carboniferous (lower)	310-354	*limestone massif and reefs*

Devonian and earlier periods - all strata concealed

been of minor importance by comparison. Some re-burial beneath sediments of Permian, Triassic, Jurassic and Cretaceous ages, i.e. from 280 to 65 million years ago, took place but not to very great depths. The last 65 million years have seen the gradual removal of this cover and the subsequent sculpting of the landscape, with a culmination of that process in the Ice Age of Pleistocene times. Erosion, before, during and after the Ice Age, has removed the remaining Millstone Grit from on top of the limestone, exposing the latter and its mineral deposits at the surface. The process of erosion is still going on

today with the Millstone Grit hills being worn away by rain and wind as well as being subject to massive landslips, as in Mam Tor. Similarly the limestone is being slowly removed by percolating rainwater dissolving out the cave systems for which Castleton is famous.

The above history of the geological evolution of the Peak District is much simplified but it should aid the reader's understanding of how the mineral deposits came into being, particularly the Blue John veins of Treak Cliff. For a better understanding first we must turn to Derbyshire's mineral deposits in general.

The Blue John deposits are but a small fraction of Derbyshire's mineral deposits and it is necessary to look at the whole picture to understand those of Treak Cliff. The limestone massif of the Peak District has some two thousand named mineral veins, most of which were originally mined for their lead ore. They fall into five categories:

1). **Rakes** are the infillings of major fractures. They are vertical or nearly so, often several kilometres in length and up to 10 m wide, though two metres is more common.

2). **Scrins** are minor fracture fillings, again vertical, usually only a few hundred metres long and less than one metre wide. Groups of scrins sometimes branch out of rakes.

3). **Flats** are mineral deposits lying more or less horizontally parallel to the layering of the enclosing limestone.

4). **Pipes** are also roughly parallel to the layering of the strata but are generally irregular in shape, often long and narrow. They are often infillings of ancient caves.

5). **Replacement deposits** are where the mineral-bearing fluids diffused through the rock and replaced it grain by grain with minerals.

All these types of deposit occur around Castleton and all have been worked to some extent for their minerals. The lead ore **galena** (lead sulphide, PbS) has been mined since Roman times, 2000 years ago, but it rarely forms more than 5% of any single deposit. It is sometimes associated with **sphalerite** (blende, also known as black jack; zinc sulphide, ZnS) though this has generally been of less economic significance. These two metallic minerals are accompanied by the gangue minerals **fluorite** (fluorspar, calcium fluoride, CaF_2), **baryte** (barium sulphate, $BaSO_4$) and **calcite** ($CaCO_3$). Usually these make up 95% of the mineral veins though the proportions vary considerably. All three gangue minerals have economic value and are still mined in Derbyshire: of them fluorspar is the most important (see below).

The minerals were deposited in the veins by layers of crystals precipitating from hot fluids and coating walls, roof and floor of fractures, filling or lining ancient caves and any other available cavity. The mineral-bearing fluids were hot solutions, known to geologists as hydrothermal. As they cooled, reacted with buried sea-water or were diluted by rain-water, the minerals precipitated from solution in order according to various factors. Often galena precipitated first, followed by either fluorspar or baryte, with calcite last, though any of the three gangue minerals could be missed out. Alternatively, in this complex equivalent of a college chemistry laboratory, the fluid flow could be rejuvenated and the whole process restarted. In short, any one vein can have repeated layers of galena, fluorspar, baryte and calcite of different thicknesses depending on variations in fluid flow and rate of crystallization. Add in earth movements causing re-opening of fractures and the resultant veins often had very complicated associations of minerals.

It was the miner's job to extract these minerals and sort out the mixture into different heaps on the surface. For centuries only the galena had any value and the rest were discarded as waste, but in the 20th century fluorspar has taken over as the chief economic product, with baryte an important second. Many old waste heaps have been re-processed for fluorspar and barytes.

Fluorite is the pure crystalline mineral, whilst fluorspar is the industrial name for calcium fluoride as it comes from the mine. Fluorite gets its name from the Latin "Fluere" meaning to flow, referring to its long-established use as a flux. Fluorspar is usually processed to yield a product at least 97% pure fluorite, which has at least 60 industrial uses, chiefly as a source of fluorine in a multitude of fluorine chemicals. Sodium fluoride is used in toothpaste and for fluoridizing water supplies as an anti-caries treatment. Sodium-aluminium fluoride is artificial cryolite, an essential catalyst in the extraction of aluminium metal from its ore. Teflon is a fluorine-derivative used to make non-stick surfaces on saucepans etc. Other uses for fluorine chemicals are in aerosols, refrigerants, detergents, specialized glasses, adhesives, fire-fighting sprays, and optical instruments. It is used in the extraction of uranium from its ores, and was once in widespread use for fluidizing slag in iron and steel-making furnaces. As the colour of Blue John is of little importance in any of these, it can be used for any of the above purposes though of course it is best reserved strictly for ornamental use.

Baryte is used in bulk as an important component of drilling mud for oil and gas wells in the North Sea and elsewhere. It is a soft mineral and lubricates the drill bits but at the same time it is heavy and the rock chips drilled away float in the baryte-rich mud and rise to the surface. Baryte is also used as a filler in paper, particularly the heavy glossy papers used in some magazines, and in paint, where it has replaced the poisonous lead once used. A thick suspension of baryte is also used as barium milk for stomach X-rays. Baryte-rich concrete is used in shielding in atomic installations. Small quantities of baryte occur in the Blue John veins of Treak Cliff though the amount of baryte is not large enough to be economically useful.

Calcite is chemically the same as limestone but it has some commercial value through its opaque white crystalline character. It is used in stucco pebble-dash for houses and in making artifical "marble" terrazo for flooring stairs, toilets etc. Small quantities are used in a plastic medium for white lines on roads. A minor use is for the ornamental white gravel on graves. Completely transparent calcite is occasionally used for optical instruments owing to its property of double refraction of light.

With these background facts in mind, where do the Blue John deposits of Treak Cliff fit into the story?

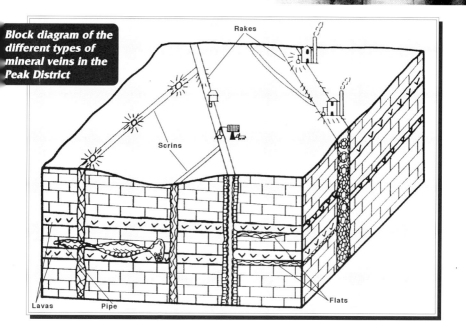

Block diagram of the different types of mineral veins in the Peak District

Rakes

Scrins

Lavas

Pipe

Flats

A "pocket" comprising an ancient cave lined with Blue John

The triangular hill of Treak Cliff has most of the five categories of mineral deposit noted above. The only example of a rake is at Odin Mine, trending almost east-west across the northern limit of the hill. Nearly two kilometres long, it is a series of closely parallel fractures aligned roughly east-west and mostly still concealed beneath the shales of Mam Tor. Lead ore has been mined there from at least the Dark Ages of the 7th to 9th centuries and probably from Roman times, for there was a Roman settlement at Brough only a little way down Hope Valley.

Mining culminated in the late 18th and early 19th centuries with thousands of tons of galena having been produced. Vast waste heaps of fluorspar, baryte, calcite and limestone accumulated, though these were largely re-worked in the 20th century when the "waste" gangue minerals became useful. Odin Mine closed in 1869 and the workings are now mostly inaccessible. Though it is so close to some of the Blue John deposits, only a matter of a few metres away, no Blue John is known to have been found in Odin Mine. This indicates that the fracture containing Odin Rake was opened after the rest of the Blue John deposits had formed, i.e. late in the mineralization sequence.

A diagram drawn in 1802 by the mineralogist John Mawe shows the disposition of the veins in relation to Mam Tor, the Winnats Pass and Long Cliff, (see page 23).

Two scrins are shown crossing the Winnats Pass though there is little to see of them. At the lower eastern end of the Pass is an extension of the Halfway House Vein in Speedwell Mine which crosses beneath the Pass and is briefly visible as a short gash high

up in the northern crags. The second is Winnats Low Scrin, with grassed-over waste heaps containing much baryte just south of the road above the Windy Bend. Both the above have a NNW-SSE trend. A third scrin not shown by Mawe is visible in a trial adit trending NNE by the roadside towards the top of the Pass. The vein consists of about 5 cm of yellowish fluorspar. None of these scrins is known to have had any Blue John.

Most of the Blue John veins are pipes and replacements. The pipes are of two types – the linings or fillings of ancient caves and the equivalent in voids between boulders in the boulder bed. The ancient caves appear to have been developed by the normal processes of cave formation in the middle of the Carboniferous period when the northern part of the Derbyshire massif had been uplifted above sea level. These caves were later enlarged by the first flushes of mineralizing fluids being rather acidic and dissolving limestone. The later fluids were not so acidic but were rich in the ions necessary to form fluorspar and layers of crystals coated every wall, roof and floor. At the same time the fluids penetrated the void system in the boulder bed and each void acted as a miniature cave, receiving a lining or filling of fluorspar. One of the most striking features of these deposits is that they are 99% fluorspar, a contrast from the rest of Derbyshire's mineral deposits. Galena is so rare it is regarded as an oddity if it is found in Blue John. Baryte and calcite almost always occur as the last crystals to form in the lining of any cavity.

Replacement deposits with blue fluorspar permeating the limestone are widespread though not enough to be economically valuable. They are generally no use for ornamental purposes as they are not banded and often full of impurities.

The pipe fillings or linings of ancient caves are present in both the Blue John and Treak Cliff Caverns and lesser amounts have been worked in the Old Tor Mine in the Winnats Pass and from several old mines on the hill top. Void fillings are much more common in Treak Cliff Cavern and some occur near Odin Mine.

Replacement deposits are spread over much of the hill.

The origin of the Treak Cliff deposits is by a fluorine-rich fluid rising into the hill whilst it was covered by shales at the end of the Carboniferous period, some 290 million years ago. There the fluid reacted with calcium-bearing groundwaters so as to precipitate fluorite, with only minor quantities of the other minerals present. It is also probable that the up-standing mass of limestone beneath its cap of shale was host to hydrocarbons, possibly comparable with a small oilfield, and that the hydrocarbons acted as catalysts. However, after precipitating the fluorspar, there would be a surplus of de-mineralized water and this was probably dispersed into the surrounding rocks. Some may have leaked to the surface as hot springs.

There are still the questions of what causes the blue colouration and why it is inter-banded with white fluorspar in the various patterns seen in Blue John. These are best looked at after discussing the detailed mineralogy of Blue John.

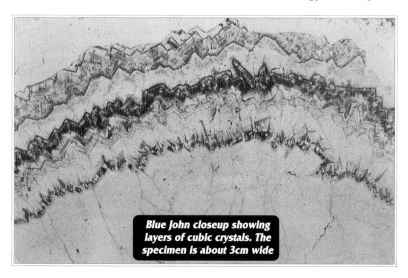

Blue John closeup showing layers of cubic crystals. The specimen is about 3cm wide

Above: Replacement Blue John with a residual section through a fossil shell still preserved in calcite Below left: A narrow portion of Millers Vein Below right: A 'pocket' void in the boulder bed lined with Cliff Blue vein & with calcite dogtooth crystals in the centre

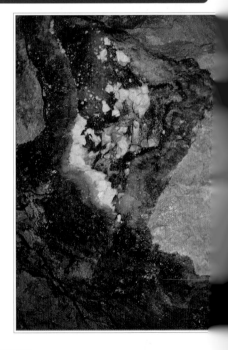

John Mawe's sketch diagram of the Blue John deposits in Treak Cliff, published in 1802

Key to Treak Cliff diagram

B	The limestone mountain where the blue fluor is found
F	Fissure between Mam Tor and the limestone
L	Long Cliff
M	Mam Tor
Mi	Miller Mine
O	Odin Mine
Ri	A rider
P	Pipe vein
S	Speedwell Mine
W	Winnats Pass
V	A vast opening (the Bottomless Pit)
R	
H	
K	
N	All Veins in Long Cliff
C	
X	

[From J. Mawe, 1802]

As with all fluorite, Blue John crystallizes in the cubic system with a molecular structure of face-centered cubes. The chemical formula is CaF_2, with a content of 51.3% calcium and 48.7% fluorine when pure. It has a specific gravity of 3.2, distinctly heavier than limestone at around 2.7, but nowhere near the weight of lead. Fluorite has a hardness of 4 on Moh's Scale of Hardness (where talc is the softest mineral at hardness 1, and diamond is the hardest at 10).

As a gemstone, fluorite has its drawbacks. Its hardness of 4 means that it is rather on the soft side compared with most gemstones and it is only cut into gems as a curiosity and not as a regular component of jewellery. The cut faces are easily scratched and soon spoilt.

The most abundant crystal habit of fluorite is simple cubes in groups of interpenetrating twins. Modifications include cubes with bevelled edges in some veins. Vicinal faces are occasionally present: they arise from an oscillation between the normal cube and one with bevelled edges resulting in crystal faces oscillating from one to the other at less than 1 mm intervals.

Blue John also crystallizes in cubes with the same modifications as above. In addition many freely grown crystals of Blue John exhibit slightly concave faces, probably due to some form of multiple lamellar twinning. Cleavage is octahedral, so that many cubes are found with the corners broken off giving cubo-octahedral forms which are sometimes passed off as octahedral crystals. Though natural octahedral crystals of fluorite have been claimed in Derbyshire, they are rare and have not yet been found on Treak Cliff. A single example of a cubic crystal with a low pyramid on each face has been found (Miller indices of 1:1:11).

The beauty of Blue John lies in its colouring and jewellery set with it is much sought after. However, it is not really for everyday use and is best kept for special occasions. Also, its cleavage means that Blue John is rather fragile and will not usually survive the knocks of regular wear. Some progress towards alleviating this problem is the use of clear quartz covers over the Blue John in jewellery, but this is not common practice and is frowned upon by some craftsmen. In short, Blue John is delicate and, as an early Duke of Devonshire once said, "Blue John is like a baby, it should not be dropped".

Cubic crystals of Blue John sometimes show contrasting edge zones. These are either where colour is concentrated yielding either pale blue cubes with dark blue edges or dark cubes with colourless edges. Sections cut through either of these types of cubes show tri-radiate patterns of colouring with diagonal zones of either dark blue or pale blue respectively.

Blue John veins grew by a series of successive coatings on fracture and cavity walls. Crystal masses grew from irregularities on those walls with lateral contact yielding a fan-like radiating material. The radiating growth layers sometimes meet their equivalents growing from opposite walls but more often small vugs or crystal-lined cavities are left in the centres of veins. A single growth layer is rarely more than 15cm thick. "Double stones" where the growths from opposite directions have met and fused may be up to 30cm across. They are uncommon though they have long been sought after by miners who wanted pieces suitable for large vases.

The real character of Blue John is the succession of blue or purplish blue crystal layers alternating with white or yellowish layers within the radiating masses. The blue bands show zig-zag sections through the cubic crystal layers with varying intensity of hue from very pale blue to almost coal black. Anything up to fifty alternating blue and white layers may be present in a single sample, though usually not more than a dozen layers are present. The blue layers are often closely packed in groups forming apparent thick dark bands.

EVIDENCE CONCERNING THE GENESIS OF BLUE JOHN

If a slice of Blue John is cut thin enough for use on a petrological microscope, layers rich in fluid inclusions can be seen. Individual fluid inclusions have a length of around 50-100 microns (a micron is one thousandth of a millimetre) and contain fluid often with a bubble like a miniature spirit level. The fluid sometimes contains minute blebs of bitumen. If a microscope equipped with special equipment for freezing the sample or for heating it is used, some deductions can be made about the nature of the fluid as the sample's temperature is raised or lowered. Firstly, it freezes at temperatures of -15 to $-30°C$ indicating a high salt content, up to ten times more than sea water. Secondly, with gentle heating the bubble gradually disappears: the point at which it does so is called the homogenization temperature and if several adjacent inclusions show the same results it is an indication of the temperature of crystallization. This is usually around 90 to $120°C$ and is similar to fluorite crystallization temperatures throughout the Peak District and in many other mineral deposits. If enough samples can be crushed in a closed vessel in such a way as to extract the fluid in usable quantities, it can be analyzed too. The fluid turns out to be a brine with a mixture of sodium and calcium chlorides and is representative of the solution from which Blue John crystallized. The brine may have hydrocarbons in suspension, as is common in the buried waters associated with many oilfields, and the blebs of bitumen seen in Blue John fluid inclusions may be the surviving traces of a long-vanished oil accumulation.

Together these observations show that Blue John crystallized from a highly saline fluid at temperatures around 90-$120°C$. Some addition to that temperature, perhaps as much as $30°C$, must be made to allow for the pressure of overlying rocks at the time of crystallization. This temperature agrees with the estimates of the temperature when the limestones lay at around 3 km depth towards

Above: Cluster of deep blue fluorite crystals Below; Left: Section through a Blue John crystal showing the blue zones and the octahedral cleavage Right: A pseudo-cubic fluid inclusion within a fluorite crystal. The bubble and a small bitumen inclusion lie within saline fluid

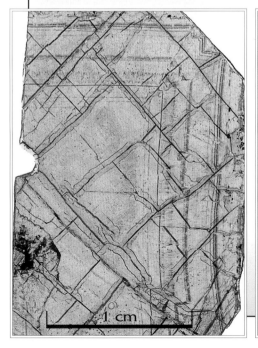

the end of the Carboniferous period, i.e. when the Millstone Grit and Coal Measures were still largely in place over the rising Derbyshire Dome.

THE COLOUR OF BLUE JOHN

The blue colouration has generally been thought to be due to the presence of inclusions or impurities. Considerable scientific investigation has been directed at finding a cause of the colour and at understanding the chemical and physical mechanisms of its development.

Microscopic examination reveals the blue colour to be due to wispy shaded areas at right angles to the cube face. Rapid successions of wispy areas give the dark blue bands. The blue wispy areas do not seem to be directly associated with the fluid inclusions: they are a separate phenomenon. Once thought to be due to an impurity of potassium permanganate (which has a characteristic purple colour) no significant manganese has been detected by detailed analysis. Another hypothesis was that the colour was due to included hydrocarbons. If Blue John is heated (before being resined for ornamental use) it gives off a slightly oily smell and loses its colour, eventually turning completely white.

However, if the white bands are separated they too will give off an oily smell. Analysis has failed to detect consistently and significantly different quantities of hydrocarbons in light and dark blue samples.

Instead the colour may be due to a physical phenomenon: crystal lattice dislocation. If the regular arrangement of atoms in a molecule is disturbed or dislocated it can distort the light transmitted or absorbed and it has been deduced that such distortions of the lattice yield the blue colour of Blue John. Lattice dislocation may be due to various causes: one hypothesis is that it is due to the presence of

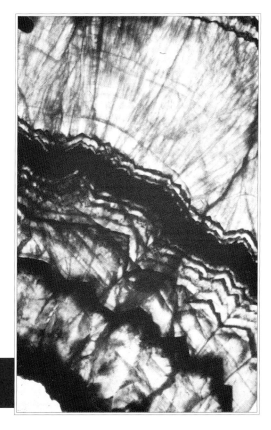

Section through Blue John showing successive blue layers

trace elements whose atoms are not quite the same size as calcium, though it is difficult to see how the decolourization experiments could be explained by these substitutions. Another hypothesis is that the dislocations are due to colloidal calcium, i.e. an excess over the ratio of atoms needed to form fluorite: this idea is favoured by several leading mineralogists. Yet another hypothesis is that radiation by radio-active elements affects the growth of the molecular lattice and small quantities of uranium are known to be present in the rocks of Treak Cliff. The basal layers of shales lying on the limestone and in some of the voids of the boulder bed contain small nodules of a phosphatic material called collophane and these contain uranium. The hot mineralizing fluids released the uranium from some of these only for it to be absorbed by hydrocarbons at the time of crystallization, including those in the process of being trapped in fluid inclusions. Neither hydrocarbons nor uranium cause the blue colour themselves but radiation damage may be significant. Furthermore, according to the rate of growth the crystals may suffer more or less dislocation damage: slowly-growing crystals will be most affected and give the bluest bands. Fast-growing crystals suffer little damage and remain white or light-coloured.

Yet another scientific study failed to detect fluid inclusions, hydrocarbons, uranium or radiation damage in the blue bands! This situation was explained by their having once contained uraniferous and hydrocarbon deposits which were washed away by the next flow of fluoride-bearing solution, leaving colloidal calcium behind, though it was still not clear how this affected the colour.

As yet, no explanation has been offered as to why the dislocations cause only shades of blue to purple. Other fluorites elsewhere are usually white or transparent, less commonly yellow, pink, red or occasionally green. Reddish colours are almost certainly due to an admixture of iron.

In spite of much scientific investigation, it seems that there is no consensus of opinion as to the cause of

A scanning electron micrograph of a Blue John cube showing it's composition of many small cubes. Note the slightly concave face on the right. Sample about 5mm wide

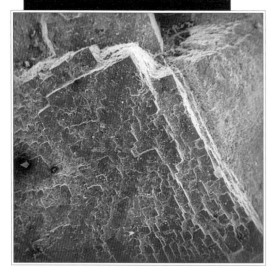

the colour. Lattice damage, with or without colloidal calcium, seems to be the most likely explanation.

URANIUM, RADIATION AND RADON

The amount of uranium in the rocks of Treak Cliff is extremely small and it is of no danger to anyone working Blue John or visiting the caves. Traces can be found in stalactites and stalagmites, averaging 6 parts of uranium in every million parts of calcium carbonate, far too little to be a health hazard.

However, where there is uranium there is also the radio-active gas radon, and in any underground cavity this may be a health hazard as it may accumulate where there is limited air circulation. Whilst the public are in no danger as they are only in the cavern for half an hour, the cave guides, particularly those who mine Blue John in the off-season, spend much longer underground and it is recommended that they limit their time spent down below. The potential risk was unknown until a few years ago and previously miners and guides spent long periods in the mines, though there is no record of any of them suffering ill-health from inhaling radon over an extended period. Today, ventilation of the caves is enhanced with the aid of fans and this reduces the radon concentration and so minimizes the guides' exposure to it.

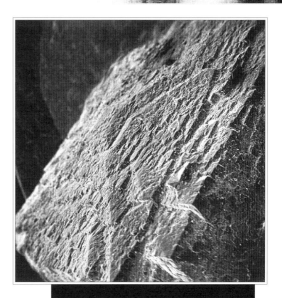

A scanning electron micrograph of a cube with a very low pyramid developed on one face. 5mm wide

DECOLOURIZATION

It has long been known that Blue John can be decolourized by heating. The craftsmen heated very dark Blue John in an oven for several hours and it came out much lighter and more attractively suitable for use in ornaments. Overheating produced useless white fluorite. It was argued that this decolourization was due to the hydrocarbons being driven off but in an experiment in the 1950s a piece of decolourized Blue John was placed in an atomic reactor - and the colour bands came back! What seemed to have happened in this experiment was that heating re-aligned the lattice dislocations and removed the colour but subjecting the sample to more radiation dislocated them again and brought back the colour bands. In fact, it was known as early as 1918 that exposure to radium could bring up coloured bands in previously colourless fluorite. Comparable experiments with rock salt have shown that it is possible to bring out similar colour bands in salt (halite) crystals by irradiating them, even though there never were any hydrocarbons present.

FLUORESCENCE

Fluorescence is the phenomenon of a mineral emitting visible light under the influence of invisible ultra-violet light. Most fluorite exhibits this phenomenon, hence its name. The fluorite crystals of the North Pennines are well known for their pale blue fluorescence under UV light, but the fluorite of the South Pennines, i.e. the Peak District, exhibits little or no fluorescence. There is a good scientific reason for this difference: the North Pennines fluorites contain a small proportion of rare earth elements, such as europium, yttrium and ytterbium, whilst those of the South Pennines are deficient in these. They substitute for calcium in the molecular lattice and as they do not fit too well they resonate and produce light under UV stimulation. Without these rare earth elements there is no resonance and hence no fluorescence. Blue John follows the South Pennine line and most does not fluoresce: a single sample yielded a pale red fluorescence, cause unknown.

THERMOLUMINESCENCE

If a substance emits light under the influence of heat it is said to be thermoluminescent. Blue John exhibits this property. If a sample of Blue John is crushed to powder and dropped on to a hot plate in

Weardale fluorite gems

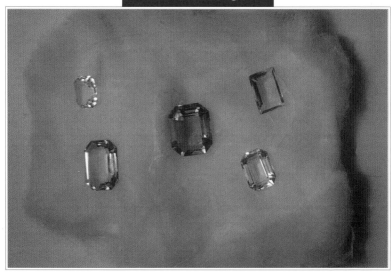

total darkness it emits flashes of light. In so doing it is releasing energy stored in its crystal structure. Scientific investigation has shown the phenomenon to be due to the presence of trace quantities of impurities, particularly the Rare Earth Elements. Only one sample of Blue John has been examined and it showed the trace quantities to be much lower than in the North Pennines, as was expected from the difference in fluorescence.

VARIETIES

The vagaries of the complex plumbing systems through ancient caves, joints and net-works of voids in the uppermost beds of limestone and the flanking boulder bed mean that the flow of fluid in any one group of voids differed from its neighbours and varied with time. Thus each void system produced its own unique pattern of colour bands. The result was the many varied patterns of colour-banding seen in the different "veins" of Blue John. These will be described in the next chapter.

An almost black variety of Blue John occurs in Treak Cliff Cavern. A thin section under the microscope shows that it is packed with minute inclusions of pyrite. It is not used for ornaments.

Another variety of Blue John is hatterel, or "tiger stone", banded yellow and colourless, sometimes with a little blue on the final layer of crystals or on their edges only. This has sometimes been mined for use in the plinths of vases, so reducing the demand for good Blue John. It is also sometimes known as Crich spar though this

form of fluorite at the Derbyshire village of Crich is generally devoid of blue colouring.

Cavities in Blue John veins may sometimes be filled or lined with calcite "dog-tooth" or "nailhead" crystals. The scalenohedral form of calcite known as dogtooth is the most common. Rosettes of baryte are far less common and usually associated with hatterel. Scattered calcite crystals may occasionally be found within Blue John. Even more rare are crystals of galena enclosed in the Blue John. As with Derbyshire mineral deposits in general, these minerals resulted from reactions between ingredients in the mineralizing fluids but the small quantities of minerals other than fluorite show that the fluids entering Treak Cliff were particularly rich in the components of the latter and deficient in the other ions.

At a few localities Blue John lies on a brownish rock layer a few centimetres thick, with a zone of replacement at the contact. This has dark blue cubes scattered through the brown material. On microscopic examination of thin sections of the latter it is found to be a meshwork of minute interlocking quartz crystals. Whilst this quartz rock is generally regarded as a metasomatic replacement (replaced molecule by molecule) of limestone, it seems possible that at least some of the quartz has recrystallized from grains of sand washed into the ancient caves just as the fluorine-bearing fluids arrived. It is just as well that quartz is not scattered through all the Blue John or it would be impossible to polish owing to the different hardnesses.

Different parts of Treak Cliff hill are characterized by different patterns of colour banding in Blue John. These are known as "veins" though they are not rakes or scrins as those terms are usually understood by the old Derbyshire lead miners. Instead the Blue John veins are the linings or fillings of ancient caves or of the voids between boulders in the boulder bed flanking the limestone. Each such void filling or lining is a "pipe" in the old lead miners' terminology, though sometimes the whole assemblage of cavity linings on Treak Cliff has been regarded either as a single major pipe vein or as several complex pipe veins.

The Blue John veins were loosely defined on their patterns of colour bands and there were traditionally said to be fourteen named veins. Each is so variable that there are really many more varieties than fourteen. It seems likely that the traditional names were originally introduced as a sales gimmick and they should perhaps not be taken too seriously. The craftsmen who work with Blue John can usually identify a sample as coming from a particular vein, i.e. from some small part of Treak Cliff. The dark bands vary from almost straight, composed of many small interpenetrating cubes lying side-by-side, or zig-zag, composed of fewer large interpenetrating cubes. The white bands range from pure white to very pale blue or sometimes yellowish or reddish hues. The yellowish or reddish tints are sometimes due to finely dispersed iron oxides but may also result from over-application of resin.

The vein banding patterns fall into groups according to different caves or mines. In 1944 John Royse claimed that the vein names were first applied by his ancestor Samuel Royse about 1830, but in fact some were in use by the 1770s, and Matthew Boulton particularly

ordered the Miller Vein for his ormolu work. Richard Brown & Son's marble works also used it in fireplaces designed by Robert Adam about 1760. Rather surprisingly, some published lists do not include the Miller Vein!

As the only known illustrations of the different veins are in a brief pamphlet privately published by E. Tunmer during World War II, some notes on the veins follow. It must be stressed that the list of named veins he illustrated does not entirely agree with the list compiled by Samuel Royse nor with the list given by his descendant, John Royse, in his booklet "Ancient Castleton Caves" in 1944. The Royses' lists also differ from that given by Arthur Ollerenshaw in the 1960s. Two other lists also differ from each other and from the Royses' lists of the veins. None of the lists was accompanied by plans of Treak Cliff or its mines showing where the named veins occurred.

So the story of fourteen named veins even had the experts differing! A full list of all the twenty or so known varieties of colour pattern is not really possible so they have been grouped into the fourteen names and an attempt to record these and their locations follows.

BLUE JOHN CAVERN

The following veins occur at progressively greater depths down to the lowest at about 60m. They all appear to be the linings of ancient cave systems.

Twelve Vein is sometimes known as the Roman Vein as it occurs in the so-called Roman workings at the foot of the entrance stairs into the Blue John Cavern, though no evidence of Roman mining has ever been found. As its name suggests, the Twelve Vein has about twelve closely packed dark purple bands with white at the top and at the bottom. It is very colourful if cut thin but rather dark in thick slices unless partly decolourized by heating.

Five Vein is similar to Twelve Vein but the bands are fused to show only as five dark purple layers, with some white or light blue between. Again it is much sought after for thin articles but liable to be too dark for thick ones. One old account does not separate Five Vein from Twelve Vein, i.e. they were sometimes regarded as variants of the same vein.

Bull Beef Vein has a white top followed by several dark purple bands separated by lighter reddish bands said to resemble the colour of "rare" beef steak. The lowest and highest bands tend to be more jagged than the straight bands in the middle. Another white band occurs at the bottom. It was probably the most popular

amongst 19th century craftsmen and clients but there is little left.

New Cavern Vein has a white band at the top, one thick white band in the centre of rather dark purple bands in the middle, with a white band at the bottom.

Organ Room Vein is rather darker than New Cavern Vein and has a group of blue bands close together in the centre, with thick white bands at top and bottom. A thin, dark blue band occurs in the top white layer.

Old Dining Room Vein has a thick white band at the top with two thin (1 mm and 2 mm) blue bands in it. A thick dark band occurs in the centre and an alternation of blue and white bands at the bottom.

New Dining Room Vein has a very thick white band at the top containing a thin (1 mm) blue band, a group of dark blue bands close together in the middle amd a narrow whitish band towards the bottom.

The two Dining Room Veins are similar and take their name from the adjacent large cavern known as Lord Mulgrave's Dining Room.

Old and New Dining Room veins occur close together off Lord Mulgrave's Dining Room and seem to be not much more than variants of the same pattern.

TREAK CLIFF CAVERN

The series of mine workings and caverns on the east face of Treak Cliff are mostly in the boulder

Twelve Vein

New Cavern Vein

The Blue John veins: Samples of Blue John showing the colour banding in the different veins. All photographs about half natural size

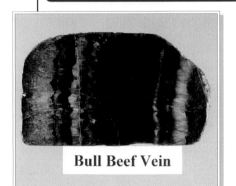

Bull Beef Vein

Old Dining Room Vein

New Dining Room Vein

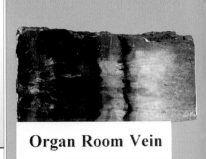

Organ Room Vein

Winnats One Vein

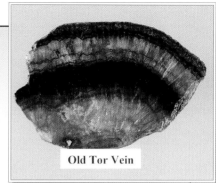

Old Tor Vein

Winnats Five Vein

Millers Vein

Cliff Blue Vein

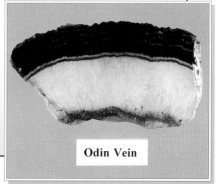

Odin Vein

bed. There are two main veins, Millers and Cliff Blue, but patches closely resemble Winnats One Vein and Twelve Vein.

Millers Vein is mainly in or near the Witches Cave. It is characterized by a thick white lower part divided by two pairs of very thin blue stripes, one stronger than the other in each pair. At the top a thick group of dark blue bands caps a thin white layer. This pattern was particularly favoured for use in 18th century vases and other ornaments. The colours show best when the stone is cut with the bands parallel to the rim.

Several variations of Millers Vein occur in adjacent parts of the Cavern. "Knife Handle Vein" is almost all white with three thin dark bands close together in the centre and a moderately thick one at the top. It is particularly favoured for knife handles and similar ornaments. This variant closely resembles Winnats One Vein. Another variant has no thin blue bands but has an enclosed layer of small scattered calcite crystals in the white fluorspar, greatly reducing its value for ornaments, though the top is fine for jewellery.

Dice Spar is Blue John, mostly from the Millers Vein, cut across the grain giving a speckled or granular appearance.

Cliff Blue Vein occurs lower down nearer the entrance to Treak Cliff Cavern and is also present in a series of near-surface patches high up on the hillside. It is a more uniform blue with dark and light jagged blue bands marking the layers of large cubic crystals. It is lighter towards the bottom. Careful selection of the direction of cutting can show the colours to advantage.

Whilst not present in Treak Cliff Cavern, a very dark blue, almost black, variety occurs on the hill top and has sometimes been called Winnats Five Vein. It sometimes has a thick white band. It was usually decolourized by heating and then resembled Cliff Blue. Much of this very dark vein was removed by fluorspar miners during World War II.

OLD TOR MINE

A pipe vein was followed down westwards from the crags high on the north side of the Winnats Pass. William Adam described going into the adit in 1838 high on the hillside on the northern flank of the Winnats Pass. Heaps of fluor were piled up along the passages. Hatterel was also obtained. A separate mine, now concealed, lies directly above the lower end of the Old Tor workings.

Old Tor Vein is in the first chamber. It has dark blue jagged bands at the base, then a thick white layer followed by a group of closely packed dark blue bands and a final white layer with a thin but double blue band at the top.

Winnats One Vein has poor quality yellowish "hatterel" at the base, then two thin blue layers followed by mostly white fluorspar with a dark band composed of three or four closely spaced blue bands in the middle, and finally very thin blue bands in a lot of white at the top.

The lower and deeper parts of the Old Tor Mine have **Winnats Second** and **Third Veins,** which are only variants of Winnats One Vein. Both tend to lack the hatterel at the base and have their central blue bands slightly more spaced out. The Winnats One Vein and its variants are rather similar to the Knife Handle variant of Millers Vein.

OTHERS

Odin Vein is not actually in Odin Mine, but Blue John occurs as void fillings in the boulder bed on the steep hillside immediately to the south. It is similar to Millers Vein but with fewer thin blue bands in the mass of white, with an intensely blue top.

Oxlow Vein is very light-coloured with scattered thin blue bands. With its less attractive colouring it was used mainly for plinths or bases of vases. No workings are known today but it is said to have been mined near the gate at the south end of the Windy Knoll field.

Windy Knoll Vein: a shaft is said to have been sunk near Windy Knoll to mine this vein but the exact site is unknown and it seems that it was long ago worked out. The pattern of colouring is said to have been rather like the Twelve Vein.

A Landscape Vein is said to occur in the Blue John Cavern in one account but it has not proved possible to identify this today.

Hatterel is a term not often used today. In the past it has been applied both to a translucent white or yellow variety of fluorspar with a thin blue crust or to a banded combination of fluorspar and baryte. The former seems the most common usage of the name Hatterel and it is either clear or cloudy yellow with many fluid inclusions, sometimes with a pattern of clear edge zones, which give a striped appearance to the cut stone: it was then known as "tiger stone". The use of both Hatterel and Tiger Stone was largely confined to plinths for vases. It was sometimes called, wrongly, Crich Spar, which is a clearer, yellowish variety of fluorspar with no blue crust.

Whilst Blue John is often claimed to be unique in its presence in Treak Cliff, Castleton, there are similar varieties of multi-coloured

banded fluorspar at other locations both in Britain and abroad. It has proved very difficult to find anything about the overseas occurrences but, so far as is known, only the Chinese material has an ornamental craft based on it. The overseas examples show subtle differences in both colours and pattern, so that it is still true to say that Blue John is unique to Derbyshire.

Above: A sample from unknown source – possibly Iran. It has a thin quartz vein cutting obliquely through the colour bands

Left: Chinese 'Blue John' carved into a penguin and a pendant

Blue fluorite is well known at several localities around the Peak District, particularly on Dirtlow Rake south of Castleton, near Matlock and at Ashover, but none of it shows a banded pattern like Blue John.

Groups of large crystals of blue fluorite are well known from Weardale in County Durham. Some crystals are up to 15 cm across and they sometimes have a coating of small quartz crystals. No banding is present though the colour does show subtle changes of shade. The Weardale material is sometimes as clear as glass and a few gemstones have been cut as curiosities (see p.30). A single bowl has been turned from the shaded blue material.

Some years ago, banded blue and yellow fluorspar specimens like hatterel were found on the waste heaps of an old copper and gold mine near Dolgellau in North Wales, but no in situ vein could be found. Whilst similar to Derbyshire material it has a pale green band in the middle. It may, of course, have dropped off the back of a lorry! No other information is available.

As noted in the section on the Roman connection, a purple-and-white banded fluorspar was mined under the name murrhine in the Roman provinces of Parthia and Carmania (southern Iran), and at least two articles have survived. Efforts to find out something about the localities concerned or about what craft is or was practised there have so far drawn a blank though geologists have reported small amounts of fluorspar mineralization around Shahrakt (formerly Sarouk) near the

Afghanistan border. Recently two specimens were obtained from the Geological Survey of Iran: one is a single pale lilac cubic crystal; the other is a fairly uniform medium blue without banding. The latter would not look out of place if dropped in workings of the Cliff Blue vein, but would be recognized as different by the experts.

Slabs of a banded purple/blue and white fluorspar are sometimes exhibited at rock-hound conventions in the United States but the exhibitors will not divulge the location other than saying "somewhere in Nevada". It could pass for Blue John except that it has a green band 1 cm wide in the midst of the blue.

A slab of a fluorspar rather like Blue John was obtained from a mineral dealer in Belgium some 30 years ago. He claimed that he did not know its location, so it may not have been from Belgium though blue fluorspar is known in the Ardennes region. Alternatively it could have come from Iran as its colouring is rather like the Roman murrhine cups noted above. It is easily distinguished from Blue John by the presence of a thin veinlet of quartz less than 2 mm wide cutting obliquely through the banding, (see page 38).

Blue fluorspar occurs widely in the Cave-in-Rock area near the Illinois-Kentucky border in the United States, where it has long been mined for industrial purposes. Occasionally it shows a coarse banding known locally as "coon-tail". No ornamental use has been recorded, but coloured fluorspar beads were found on the Kincaid archaeological site nearby. These were apparently valued by Indians around 1450 to 1600 A.D. but whether they made them is not known: it is possible that they were water-worn pebbles picked up in a stream bed.

Some of the world's richest resources of fluorspar are in Mexico. Blue crystals are well known but not banded material.

A banded fluorspar with lilac/pink and yellowish bands has been used for centuries in small quantities in inlaid marble tables etc (pietra dura) in Italy under the name Smeraldina. Whilst similar to Blue John the colouring is much more lilac to pink. As is so often the case, the "secrets" of its occurrence are closely guarded and it has proved impossible to find anything out.

China is the world's foremost producer of fluorspar and it is mined at numerous localities for industrial purposes. Some 40 years ago a consignment of fluorspar received from China by a Derbyshire iron-smelting company contained banded blue and white material very like Blue John. The similarity was soon recognized by the Derbyshire workmen and this led to small consignments being obtained by mineral dealers for use as a substitute for Blue John in jewellery. The colour varies from intense blue to a bluish-green. Banded fluorspar of this type is produced from the Deqing Fluorite Mine north of MoGan Mountain, Deqing County, Zhejiang Province, near China's east coast. The fluorspar occurs in veins cutting volcanic and sedi-mentary rocks of Jurassic age. It is used for metallurgical purposes, and for building materials, presumably in cement manufacture. Coloured fluorspar is also produced at Tscheng Ting in the Tai-Hang-Shan mountains, Shensi Province, some 550 km southwest of Beijing, but whether this can substitute for Blue John is not known. The Deqing material is exported to Japan, America and Europe.

Apart from these industrial applications some blue-banded fluorspar is apparently used for ornamental purposes and can occasionally be found in the jade shops in the tourist areas of China. The writer bought a carved penguin of Chinese "Blue John" in a shop in Beijing, the only article of this material they had on display. Horse's heads and other animals carved from Chinese blue banded fluorspar have been seen in displays in jeweller's shops in Italy and are also used as attractive foils for jewellery in shops throughout Europe. An unfinished pendant was obtained in Britain and probably came from China. Pairs of earrings made from Chinese "Blue John" were recently on sale in East Anglian amber shops.

Beads of various materials including purple fluorspar were found by archaeologists in a Neolithic site south of Hangchow Bay in the same Province as the Deqing Mine, so there seems to be a long history of fluorspar ornaments in China but it has proved difficult to obtain any information.

Since Blue John only occurs in small masses lining ancient caves or in voids in the limestones and boulder bed of Treak Cliff there is no call for large scale mining. Each piece of Blue John has to be extracted carefully by hand, with no blasting by explosives as these would open the cleavages effectively shattering the semi-precious stone and rendering it useless for ornaments or jewellery. Instead the usual mining practice is to extract the limestone around the Blue John and so release the latter from its enclosing rock.

Two methods of extraction are in use: wedging and drilling. In wedging any joints in the limestone have iron wedges driven in by hammering until the joint-blocks come apart. Drilling is more sophisticated. Hammering the drills was once done by hand, but nowadays it is more commonly done by electric percussion drill – rather like an oversize Black & Decker hammer-drill. Holes about 2.5cm diameter are drilled in for about 15 to 30cm usually in lines of up to a dozen. These can then be used for iron wedges but often wooden plugs are driven in. A thinner iron wedge can then be driven into the wooden plugs in a traditional method known as "plug and feather". A line of such wedges hammered in turn will split the rock. Alternatively, the series of wooden plugs can be wetted and left to swell overnight or perhaps for a few days. The pressures exerted by swelling wooden plugs can split the rock as effectively as iron wedges.

The ancient lead miners means of splitting the rock known as fire-setting was occasionally used to obtain Blue John. A wood fire was built against the limestone and left to burn overnight. The heat expanded the rock and a bucket of water thrown over it in the morning opened cracks ready for wedges.

Another method of splitting the rock is to pack the drill holes with lime. This too swells as it is wetted and cracks the limestone. The method is sometimes known as lime-blasting but it is rarely used today.

In the 18th century, some Blue John was obtained by a different method: sifting through the sediments which had been washed into the caves during the Ice Age. Much lead ore was obtained by the same method in the 18th century and earlier. In these ancient times cave-forming waters passed through parts of the mineral deposits and dissolved the surrounding limestone. Any attached galena or Blue John was insoluble and fell off in lumps to be buried in the silts and clays washed in from the surface. The miners simply went through the sediments with their hands or, occasionally, with wooden spades, until they found hard lumps. Scratching it or trimming a corner off would soon tell if the lump was Blue John, lead ore or limestone, and the former two were then carried outside to be washed. Much of the entrance series of Treak Cliff Cavern still has such sediments forming the floor but they have long ago

Hand-drilling at the margin of a Blue John vein

been sorted through for residual lumps of Blue John.

Whether obtained by sifting sediments, by wedging or by drilling and splitting the rock, the next step is to clean the Blue John. After washing away unnecessary sediment, excess limestone was once trimmed from the Blue John by hammer and chisel but today it is usually cut off with a rock saw. Some of the washing and trimming was once done underground but most is done outside today. After cleaning the Blue John is stored for a year or two until it is thoroughly dry. If any attempt to work the Blue John is done whilst it is still wet, the heat generated by the friction of grinding is liable to open the cleavages so reducing the translucency and ruining the appearance.

The quantity mined each year is small. Today perhaps half a ton is the total annual production, though no official figures are released. Back in the late 18th century leases from land-owners restricted output to 20 tons per annum, though there are no recorded figures for output. Nor is there any documentary evidence of how the limitation was enforced. Some idea of the quantities involved in 1768 comes in a letter from Matthew Boulton (see later) in which he was trying to lease the mines. So far as is known he was unsuccessful and instead the next year he bought a consignment of Blue John weighing 14 tons from John Platt at £5-15-6 per ton. This may well have been the greater part of a year's output. In 1892 the output is said to have been limited to 3 tons per annum.

Making a few estimates based on the above figures, it appears that the total production of Blue John for ornamental purposes in the 250 years up to the present is somewhat less than 2000 tons.

There have also been some periods of mass production. From 1919 Messrs G.T.West & Co of Liverpool obtained a lease and worked Blue John for use as ordinary fluorspar in blast furnaces. An inclined haulage railway was built down the face of Treak Cliff to a loading bay for lorries on the roadside. A chute was also built close to the present entrance to Treak Cliff Cavern. The expense of constructing such facilities suggests that substantial quantities were involved. Blue John fluorspar was obtained from the Witches Cave of Treak Cliff Cavern and from several small open quarries on the hillside above. No record of quantities appears to have survived but a reasonable guess would suggest that some hundreds of tons of blue fluorspar went into furnaces. Some is even said to have been exported to America. West & Co marketed good Blue John separately and at least two lorry loads went to Grant's marble and spar manufactory at Watcombe, near Torquay. Several of the miners were local men and they knew the value of top quality Blue John and quietly "hid" some of it for future retrieval. Most was indeed recovered later but one hidden cache is reputed to be buried somewhere. It was during West & Co's operations in 1926 that the breakthrough was made to the stalactite caves which now form part of the tourist route. There is some doubt as to whether mining Blue John would be financially viable without being linked to the tourist caves.

During World War II a further attempt was made to extract Blue John fluorspar for industrial use. Czech refugees were put to work by the Ministry of Supply on the flat top of Treak Cliff to mine by opencast methods. A log washer was erected by the stream close to Odin Mine (also used in post-war years to process fluorspar brought from Bradwell Moor). To judge from the size of the remaining pits only a small quantity was ever produced. The Blue John there is very dark and generally of rather poor quality for ornaments so there was no great loss of good stone. The Czechs also sank a shaft near Odin Mine and drove a short adit into the side of Odin Gulley, again with a short inclined railway down to the road, but the tonnages produced were never great and the whole operation was financially unsound.

Illegal mining of Blue John from Old Tor Mine in the Winnats Pass took place in the 1970s and some tons of good stone were extracted. The operation came to an end when the culprits were caught red-handed (blue-handed?), taken to court and heavily fined.

After Blue John has been mined it is stored for at least a year until it is thoroughly dry. The pieces are then sorted into large and small, respectively suitable for vases, bowls and other large articles or for jewellery and small articles.

Large pieces of Blue John are less easy to obtain from the mine and much care is taken in selecting pieces for the most appropriate end product. Each piece is studied as to what sort of vase or bowl can be turned from it. It is sized up to minimize waste and to exhibit the banded pattern to best advantage. As far as possible pieces are worked so that the banding is parallel to the rim. A bowl with banding going obliquely across it is generally less attractive than one with the banding round the rim.

The next step is to cut off unwanted material and to produce a rough shape. In the early days this was done with a mallet and chisel but today a rock saw is used. This is normally a disc of carborundum, a synthetic material composed of silicon carbide, mounted on a lathe, though diamond-edged bronze discs are occasionally used. The carborundum discs are about the size of the old long-playing gramophone records and are used wet, with a drip feed of water to keep both the Blue John and the cutting edge cool. Alternatively the saws may be run through a shallow water bath though this tends to produce a lot of spray. The discs are effectively very thin grinding wheels and they grind their way through the Blue John. Earlier methods used a copper disc running through a bath of mixed fine emery powder and water, but this was rather slow and needed frequent recharging. It was even slower when powered by a foot treadle in the days before electric tools became available.

Once roughed out, the Blue John was treated with resin to harden it. The stone was heated in an oven or on a hotplate until it was just too hot to handle and resin was melted into its surface. The resin filled in cleavages and other growth defects, held the Blue John together and tended to increase translucency. Resining was usually done after sawing as the resin tended to clog the cutting edge of the saw if done first. Care had to be taken that the stone did not get too hot or the resin burnt within it and gave an unpleasant brown colour. Indeed, excessive heating caused the resin to burn so much as to turn the stone black. With large pieces the resin did not penetrate far enough and it was often necessary to reheat and re-resin the article several times during manufacture.

The resin traditionally used was amber-yellow pine resin. In recent years, however, various synthetic epoxy-resins have come into use, and the technique today is to impregnate the Blue John with araldite. This is done in a vacuum oven and considerable skill is needed in mixing the araldite and in judging the right temperature and timing to get the required results. Araldite is expensive too!

The rough-out is mounted on a lathe and turned to the required shape. The mounting used to be done with a home-made cement used to stick the article on to a chuck. The cement was a mixture of resin, tallow and plaster of Paris melted together; rock-hard when cold, it is plastic and sticky at hand-hot temperatures and many old articles of Blue John were stuck together or mounted with it. Wire was often bound round the outsides of bowls and vases as the resin did not penetrate deeply enough to reduce the chance of shattering whilst turning. The use of araldite does away with the need for wire-binding.

In the smaller workshops the lathes were treadle-powered until about 40 years ago and the cutting tool was a steel bar about 2 feet long and a half-inch square with a pointed or wedge-shaped end. Great skill was needed to apply such a cutting tool accurately whilst pumping one foot up and down on the treadle and it was not uncommon to have one person treadling whilst another applied the tools. The larger workshops mainly used water-power or, occasionally, steam power. Nowadays an electric lathe is the normal practice but the Blue John is stuck to the chuck with the traditional adhesive. Clamping it into jaws leads to many breakages. A steel cutting tool clamped to the lathe mounting is gradually applied and the shape is turned out in a standard lathe-working fashion. Turning out the rough shape is done dry but surface grinding is done wet to keep the stone cool.

When the article has been turned to its final shape its surface is progressively smoothed by applying small pieces of grinding stone held in the fingers. Further impregnation with resin or araldite may be necessary as the surface is prepared for the final polishing stages. Polish is attained in two stages. The penultimate surface treatment was light grinding with a Water-of-Ayr stone, a very fine-grained natural material, or often applied today by wet-and-dry emery paper, 1200 grade, used wet. A stage of "leading" with paper-thin lead sheets wrapped round the fingers was once used but not necessary today. Then comes the polishing itself - putty powder applied to a moist piece of felt wrapped round the fingers. Putty powder is in fact very finely crushed tin oxide, and nothing to do with putty which is crushed chalk in linseed oil. Occasionally jewellers' rouge (finely ground iron oxide) or crocus powder (chromium oxide) are used instead but they are less popular as they tend to lodge in surface cracks and discolour the stone. Polishing by putty powder is where the craftsman's skill is at its highest. No frictional heat must be allowed. No grit or dirt must be allowed in or it scratches the surface. As the stone's surface reaches a perfect polish it is washed gently with clean water and when this does not improve the appearance, then polishing is complete. Polishing a large article may take several hours.

Occasionally the final stages of fine grinding and polishing revealed flaws in the Blue John, necessitating filling in. If the flaws were small enough, shellac sufficed and was melted in with the end of a heated spatula. Larger flaws were sometimes filled with ground-up galena in shellac or resin. Occasionally pieces of Blue John were inlaid to fill the flaws. The final effect was rather like the rare crystals of galena found naturally in Blue John and became a potential selling point. This craftsman's trick was noted as early as 1784.

Many of the late 18th century ornaments were made of solid Blue John as methods of hollow turning had not been developed then. A few had shallow imitation hollows turned in the necks. Solid Blue John, unfortunately, does not transmit light very well and the results were rather dark.

By the end of the 18th century hollow vases were more common. Some large examples, made for stately homes, were built up out of a series of rings of Blue John dovetailed and stuck together. The best craftsmen could turn the inside in such a way as to save the core and lift it out for use in a

Assessing a piece of Blue John to judge the best way of cutting a bowl from it

Grinding Blue John into shape

smaller ring. The joins between rings are disguised as much as possible by hiding them in ring-mouldings, but breaks in the colour banding still show where the joins are. Large vases and other ornaments usually had a steel pin inserted from the underside of the bowl, down the centre of the stem into the base. Occasionally these have a screw thread and a nut at the base.

Turning large pieces on a treadle lathe was a risky business with breakages all too common, so as far as possible some form of power was applied to give the craftsman better control over his cutting tool. A few early workshops had "engines" but no record survives

of what these might have been. Some workshops certainly had water-wheels for power, as used by Henry Watson at his black marble works at Ashford-in-the-Water. Brown's used water-power and later steam-powered machinery in Derby.

Some 18th or 19th century large vases show grooved ridges or flutings down the lower part of the cup. As these cannot be turned on a lathe, they had to be chiselled out before being fine-ground and polished, all by hand.

Many of the large antique vases to be seen in stately homes have a heavy square plinth of Blue John. As these tend to use up rather a lot of Blue John, plinths were often made of solid blocks of low quality Blue John or were veneered with it using mitred joints at the corners; sometimes the yellowish Crich spar was used instead. The veneered plinths had four rectangular slabs cut to meet at the corners and the centre was filled with plaster of Paris. The caps and base plates of plinths were often squares of black marble but some have wood painted black or veneered with tortoiseshell or alternatively white marble or alabaster. Occasionally Wedgwood plaques were fixed on to plinths but the intense blue of these tends to detract from the darker blue-purple of Blue John.

As noted elsewhere herein, the clear to yellow Crich Spar was used for plinths. It was also turned into a variety of vases in its own right presumably because blocks were easier to come by than Blue John. A few Crich Spar vases contain patches of the lead ore, galena. Blue John ornaments are also known to have lead ore but it is very rare in its natural state and it is not unknown for damaged vases to have been repaired by filling with lead metal in simulation of galena.

Making a Blue John ornament as described above may not sound very difficult but it is the craftsman's judgement which is vital at several stages and few people have the patience or skill to do the work today. The craft requires skill in selecting and sizing up what can be made from any particular piece; cutting to rough shape; heating and resining; mounting on the lathe and applying the cutting tool; fine-grinding and polishing. In the old days of treadle lathes

and hand-held tools, as many bowls were broken as finished. Even today a fair number of what are started are never finished owing to flaws in the stone or to slight errors of judgement in the turning.

Blue John jewellery is generally easier to deal with. Usually starting with fist-sized or smaller pieces of Blue John, they are sawn into slabs about 5-10 mm thick and then resined. The slabs are then cut into sets of rectangles 2-3cm wide and 5-6cm long, making sure that the colour banding runs across the stones. Thick bands of pure white fluorspar are of course rejected. Each piece is then held between the fingers and shaped against a small grindstone on the lathe. Batches are prepared to fit equivalent ring or brooch settings. Each is tried into a setting several times until a good fit is attained. After re-resining the stones are fine-ground against a Water-of-Ayr stone or rubbed down by hand with wet-and-dry paper, 600 and 1200 grades. The polish is obtained by holding the stone against a rotating buff of compressed felt on the lathe, wetted and with putty powder applied.

Ring and brooch stones are usually flat underneath and rounded on top, i.e. cabochon-cut. Facetting is rarely attempted and not generally of much use as Blue John does not provide internal reflections in the same way as diamonds. The ring mounts are generally hollow-backed so that light can pass through to the skin of the wearer's finger and then be reflected back. If solid-backed mounts are used the stone should be as light as possible as a dark stone with no light reflected back through it will look even darker and less attractive. In some cases of solid-backed mounts the Blue John insert is painted white on the under side to increase reflectivity. Blue John brooches are again best with hollow-backed mounts worn on light coloured clothing. Mounts are generally silver though gold is becoming popular today.

Blue John stones cut for jewellery are fixed into the settings either with cement or by having claws or lips of metal which can be bent over the margin of the stone.

Amongst other small articles are pendants. Pear-drop shaped pendants have to be drilled to affix a silver or gold loop to hang it on to a chain. Brass is regarded as too cheap for quality Blue John work. Drilling is a delicate operation using a needle-drill on a vertically mounted drilling machine. It is usually done before final polishing as breakages are common and early drilling means that fewer articles have to be taken as far as the polishing stage. Knife handles of Blue John are attractive but not often made today as breakages are too common during drilling: such handles are not really for everyday use as the leverage applied in cutting anything soon breaks them. Small fruit knives were the most common but even they should be treated with care. Sticking the tang into the handle was done with the old-fashioned home-made cement to allow for the delicate positioning.

The stems of vases have to be treated in much the same way as knife-handles, i.e. drilled to take a steel pin. This has to be long enough to go into the underneath of the bowl and into the top of the base plate. When all is stuck together with cement it provides a secure support.

Blue John is also used for inlay work. From the late 18th century until very early in the 20th century Blue John was often inlaid into the many articles made of Ashford Black Marble with geometrical, patchwork or floral patterns. It was particularly favoured for floral displays with blue flowers or grapes. As with jewellery, the Blue John inserts (and other coloured stones) were shaped by fine grinding to fit sockets cut out of the marble with small chisels or drills. The sockets were cut out to depths of around 3 to 5mm by tools comparable to modern dentists' drills. The inserts were mounted by a pinch of powdered cement in the socket and a warm iron used to melt it through the insert; when cold the insert was safely stuck in. Epoxy-glues mean that heating is unnecessary but they make it difficult to lift the stone out for later re-adjustment or repair. The final polish was applied to the Blue John and marble as one unit. This type of work is rarely done today as it is very time-consuming and expensive.

Panels or other designs of Blue John were also inlaid into marble fireplaces, particularly in the late 18th century stately homes around Derby. There was some risk that the heat of the fire would melt the cement so that the Blue John would fall out but designers took this into account and kept the Blue John at a safe distance.

Since Blue John slabs have colouring comparable with stained glass it is not surprising that a few stained glass windows have been made of Blue John. The Blue John may either be glued to glass panels or, if it is thick enough, it is left free-standing.

Another type of inlay work that is still in use is the fitting of rims of Blue John round white onyx articles such as clocks, cigarette boxes, finger bowls and ash-trays. The contrast of Blue John and the white stone is particularly attractive (see p.94). The methods used are much the same as with inlay work in black marble.

Craftsmen are also called on today to carry out repairs to broken or damaged articles. In many cases completely new pieces of Blue John will have to be turned or cut to match the rest of the article. New ring or brooch stones are often in demand and easily satisfied, but the most common repairs needed are to broken vase stems. These can be taken apart by melting the old cement and refitting the steel rod down the centre. Though broken stems may sometimes be simply stuck together, it is usual to make a new piece which will require drilling out and fitting a new pin. Vases with chipped lips are all too common. Whole new lip pieces may have to be turned or sometimes the old lip can be trimmed down, re-ground and re-polished to yield an article with a smaller diameter. Alternatively the cavity in the rim may be ground smooth and a new piece inlaid, using modern "super-glue" adhesives.

Polishing the top section of a large vase

Assembling the parts of a large vase

Carved Roman Blue John cup, possibly from a grave on the Turko-Syrian border

The discovery of Blue John is often credited to the Romans. They had a fort at Brough only some 4 km down Hope Valley and mined lead in the hills around Castleton and Bradwell so it might seem reasonable to think that they knew about Blue John and obtained it for use in Rome, but no evidence to support such a suggestion has yet come to light. They probably used local labour so that their direct involvement in mining was at the administrative and military level. The lead-rich mineral vein at Odin Mine is likely to have attracted the Romans to Castleton and, as far as we know, Blue John does not occur there so it is possible that they did not meet this unusual mineral variety.

The story that the Romans used Blue John can be set aside by a number of other observations.

No Blue John has ever been reported from any archaeological investigation of a Roman site in Britain and, surely, if Blue John was mined then, pieces would have been found by archaeologists in the ruins of nearby Roman settlements.

A trackway branching off the top of the Winnats Pass on to the top of Treak Cliff is known locally as the Roman Hollow, but no evidence that it is of Roman origin has yet been produced and it is far more likely to be a mediaeval trackway. Similarly the so-called Roman workings in the Blue John mine have not yielded any specific evidence such as coins or pottery of Roman date.

There is, however, one intriguing record for which we may never know the answer. The Roman Emperor Septimius Severus died whilst visiting Britain and his remains were cremated in York and the ashes placed in an "urn of purple stone". Whilst it is tempting to think this might have been Blue John, it is just as likely to have been amethystine quartz and so it is unlikely that the matter can be resolved.

The story of the Roman connection can be traced back only as far as William Adam's book "Gem of the Peak" published in 1843. Adam was a craftsman and entrepeneur based in Matlock, and the mid 19th century was a time when there was great public interest in antiquities. It seems very likely that Adam saw a potential for boosting his sales by telling this "Roman" story. No earlier book or manuscript has been found to mention any Roman connection.

Part of the legend of the Romans having mined Blue John has long been said to arise from Blue John vases being found in the ruins of Pompeii, which was overwhelmed by the eruption of Vesuvius in A.D.79. But modern investigations in the various archaeological museums around Pompeii have failed to reveal any such vases. Instead there are vases made of banded amethystine quartz which looks rather like Blue John to those less familiar with it – these vases are not Blue John and the stone did not come from Derbyshire. There is also a matter of chronology – the Romans did not reach the Peak District until about 12 years before Pompeii was overwhelmed, so it

leaves only a few years for a craft and trade to be established between Castleton and Rome, which seems unlikely.

The noted Sheffield cave explorer, J.W.Puttrell, who explored the Blue John Cavern in 1902 and gave many lectures on Blue John up to the 1930s, made a special visit to Italy in 1935 in order to find out something about the alleged Blue John vases in museums near Pompeii and Naples. He was unable to find any such vases, and the museum directors knew nothing about Blue John.

The confusion of Blue John with banded amethyst is compounded by an 18th century name for Blue John being "radix amethysti" and one Blue John vase seen by the writer has an engraved brass plate fixed to the plinth stating that it was made of "Amethystine Quartz, found in Castleton in the 17th century": both identification and date are wrong!

The Roman writer Pliny, who described the eruption of Vesuvius in A.D. 79, also wrote a substantial work on natural history, including accounts of various minerals and gemstones. Amongst these he noted a material which he called **murrhine** and which sounds very much like Blue John. Translation of his words from Latin produces several uncertainties, but a few examples may be cited: "approaching the colour of wine", "great variety of colours and the wreathed veins....present shades of purple and white with a mixture of the two; the purple gradually changing as it were to a fiery red and the milk white assuming a ruddy hue". These descriptions certainly sound like

Above left: Roman cantharus cup with carved handles

Above right: Banded amethystine quartz cantharus said to be from near Pompeii

Opposite: Pale green fluorspar bowl, possibly of Roman date, said to have been found in Egypt (now in the Ashmolean Museum, Oxford)

Blue John or a similarly coloured mineral but they are not sufficient to prove it so. Pliny also commented that "murrhine vessels were for taking drinks that are either hot or cold"; "a person of consular rank grew so passionately fond of his cup as to gnaw its edges – this tended to enhance its value" – one could bite pieces out of the rim of a fluorspar cup, but not from amethyst. "Nero had the fragments of a broken cup preserved in an urn". The Emperor Nero is reputed have paid a vast sum for one cup and he is said to have resorted to rather underhand methods to acquire others. Amongst Pliny's comments is that wine tasted better from murrhine cups, and if the craftsmen then used resin for binding the stone as modern craftsmen do, then the taste of resin might have affected the wine.

Pliny made no mention of a British source for murrhine but said quite clearly that the finest quality came from the empire of the Parthians and from Carmania, two Roman provinces in what is now southeastern Iran (Carmania is in effect a subdivision of Parthia). Other Roman writers made much the same comments and said that it was first brought to Rome after Pompey the Great's campaign to conquer Persia in 62-61 B.C.

Whilst nothing is known of the exact Iranian locality, mineral deposits with small quantities of purple/blue fluorspar have been found near the town of Sarouk (= modern Shahrakt, close to the border with Afghanistan).

Some writers have ignored Pliny's statement that the source of murrhine was in Parthia (i.e. Iran) and have argued that it could only have come from Derbyshire. However, Pliny's comments clearly indicate that there was a source of a banded crystalline material very like Blue John in Iran.

Whilst Pliny's description does not prove that murrhine was fluorspar, the discovery in 1919 of two banded purple and white fluorspar cups in a Roman tomb at Kotor near the border of Syria and Turkey supports his story. This locality is halfway between Iran and Rome so the cups could have been buried en route to the latter. The two cups were found by a Turkish army engineer about 1919 and were sold to a Greek dealer. One is a two-handled cup of cantharus style and it was brought to Britain in the 1920s and is now in the British Museum; the other was in a private collection in Brussels in the 1950s. Their colouring is rather like the Bull Beef vein but they show a feature not known in any Blue John article. They have been carved with their handles part of the same piece of stone as the cups, i.e. not turned on a lathe. The single-handled cup, last heard of in Brussels, has also been carved with a design of grape vines in low relief on the outer surface. It suggests that there were craftsmen skilled in working fluorspar in the Middle East in Roman times.

A lump of blue, red and purple translucent stone thought to be fluorspar was reported in J.H. Middleton's book on "Ancient Rome in 1888" to have been dug up in the Marmoratum in Rome, and was cut into slabs to line the high altar of the Church of Jesu.

A small fluorspar bowl obtained from a dealer in antiquities in Cairo in 1953 may have emanated from the same source and craftsmen. It has a pale green tint to an otherwise colourless transparent background. It was once said to have a very pale purple band but this is not visible today. It is 6.75 cm in diameter, 4.3 cm high, and shows polishing marks suggestive of having been turned on a lathe. It is now in the Ashmolean Museum in Oxford. Whilst thought to be of Roman date there is no direct proof.

Thus, it seems clear that no evidence of the Romans having mined Blue John at Castleton is yet forthcoming and its earliest known use as an ornamental stone is in the mid 18th century.

How the potential of Blue John for ornaments was first discovered is a matter shrouded in mystery. The Roman connection seems now to be totally discredited so we must turn to more recent historical data.

As small veins of blue fluorspar outcrop on Treak Cliff, near Odin Mine and on the Old Tor overlooking the Winnats Pass, it would have been visible to any observant person from early times. Fallen rocks with blue spar would easily have been noticed by travellers using the Pass. Even so, the following records are all we have to go on concerning its presence and use.

In his history of metals "Metallographia" (1671), J. Webster discussed "fluores" and said: "some of the very colour of Amethyst, that, if polished and set in rings - were able to deceive a very skilful lapidary". Unfortunately Webster gave no locality but his comment does indicate that the idea of making blue fluorspar ringstones as a substitute for amethyst had occurred to him. Whether anyone actually did so as early as 1671 is not known.

Celia Fiennes, in her book "Through England on a Side-Saddle" (1697), mentioned seeing azure spar in Derbyshire, though she did not say where; nor did she say anything about it being used for ornaments or jewellery. Charles Leigh in his "Natural History of Lancashire, Cheshire and the Peak District" (1700) recorded "sapphirine and azure spar" in Derbyshire but again failed to say whether it was used in any way.

By contrast almost every book on the Peak District from the 1760s onwards noted both mining and making ornaments and jewellery from Blue John. Many great stately homes in the 1760s and their owners patronized the crafts in the surrounding district. In particular Kedleston Hall, near Derby, was built for Lord Scarsdale around 1760 and the architect Robert Adam designed marble fireplaces with Blue John inlays and panels for his Lordship. They were made at Joseph Hall's marble works near St Helen's Church in Derby and installed in 1762 (taken over by his brother-in-law Richard Brown soon afterwards, and still later operated by the founder's great-grandsons, Joseph & Thomas Hall, about 1850). Several other mansions around Derby also had fireplaces with Blue John panels or inlays. One in the Friary Hotel, Derby, can be dated to about 1760 (see further discussion under Fireplaces).

As described elsewhere in this book, Matthew Boulton often used Blue John and is thought to have made a candelabrum for Lord Dundas in 1762 out of a Blue John core surrounded by the gilded brass frame known as ormolu.

Richard Brown's supply of Blue John was obtained from a Mr Bradbury of Castleton, though it is not known whether he was a miner, mine-owner or a merchant, or possibly some combination of all three. It is reputed to have been transported from Castleton to Derby in a locked cart as it was so valuable. It is worth noting that most of the Blue John used by Brown came from the Cliff Blue and Millers Veins in what is now Treak Cliff Cavern.

Another approach to finding out how Blue John came into use is to study lead mining records. These include both family documents in various Archive Collections as well as the Barmasters' Books in which all lead mining transactions were supposed to be recorded. There was considerable lead mining activity on Treak Cliff around 1709-1710 with a dispute over mining rights at Waterhull (= Water Hole?) Mine, later also known as Tre-Cliffe Mine. These seem to have been different parts of what we now know as the Blue John Cavern. Waterhull Mine was apparently entered through a sink-hole east of the present cave entrance and extended down into the Inferior Gallery, a part of the cavern not seen by the public today: Tre-Cliffe Mine was not Treak Cliff Cavern as known today but the present entrance to the Blue John Cavern and the passages at the foot of the entrance stairs, now the Twelve Vein and Five Vein workings. The two series were eventually linked via the Bull Beef Vein workings and the names Waterhull and Tre-Cliffe seem to have been applied interchangeably to both. The present visitors' route down the Pothole and into the caverns beyond was engineered about 1836.

Also around 1709-1710, there were four lead mines at work on the northeastern slope of Treak Cliff in New Nab and Trake Cliffe Grove veins. The exact positions of these are uncertain, but it is likely that New Nab was on the steep slope south of Odin Mine whilst Trake Cliffe Grove was equivalent to the Old Miller Mine. The New Nab vein seems to have been a pipe and scrin roughly parallel to Odin Rake whilst the Trake Cliffe Grove was a pipe vein in lead miners' terms. In 1709 it was noted that 12 men and 4 women were working at New Nab. A New Gate Mine worked a pipe somewhat to the north of Trake Cliffe Grove where there is much disturbed ground with a small cave beneath.

The present site of Treak Cliff Cavern was apparently two separate mines in one pipe vein, Trake Cliffe Grove. Old Miller Mine was being worked by 1709 but Cliffside was later, first recorded in 1784. Cliffside is the part of the present Treak Cliff Cavern nearest the entrance whilst Old Miller Mine is higher up.

More than 175 tons of lead ore was produced from the Waterhull mines in 1709-1710. It came largely from loose lumps in the silt and clay fill in the pipe vein caverns, not from rakes or scrins. The lead miners could not have failed to see the Blue John veins, but unfortunately the mining records are concerned with lead only and they do not mention whether Blue John was mined at all. However, by the 1760s the Millers Vein of Blue John was particularly favoured for fireplaces and ormolu. It is not known who the Miller of Millers Vein and Miller Mine was as the name does not appear anywhere else in the archives.

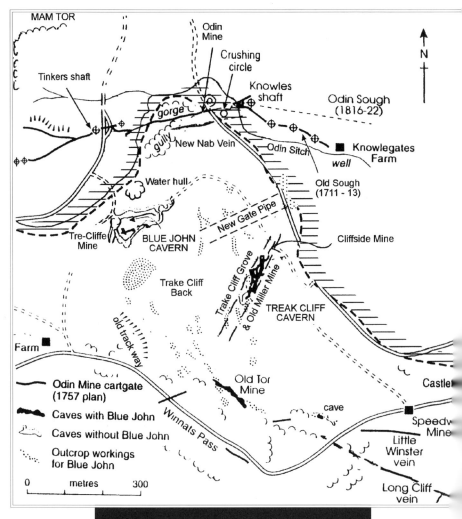

Veins and mines known in the late 18th century

The Barmaster's Book noted on 30th June 1753 that a "Founder Meer for Isaac and Jno Royse an old scrin on Trake Cliffe Back at Windyates Door called Ever-lasting" had been registered as a lead mine. The site of this mine is unknown but Trake Cliff Back has no scrins, only pipe veins, so Blue John may have been the real target and registration as a lead mine was a precaution against take-overs!

In 1748, Henry Watson established a water-powered marble mill at Ashford-in-the-Water for working the black marble mined there. Soon afterwards he had the idea of inlaying panels of coloured stones into black marble, possibly as a result of what he had heard about Italian inlay work from gentry who had done the Grand Tour of Classical Europe. Blue John was one of these coloured stones but when he first started inlaying it is not known. A few years later an entry in the Barmaster's book in August 1765 noted:

"Mr Wattson of Ashford set five pairs of stows on the north side of Windygates (=Winnats) for an old pipe ranging northwestwardly. Also two pairs on the west of the same for another old pipe ranging as above. And two pairs more on the west side of the last two pairs for new, the Grace of God and what he could find. Also set by Mr Wattson aforesaid one pair of Stows on Trake Cliff Top for an old pipe. And also six pairs of stows set by him for new or what he could find ranging from south to north".

Thus Henry Watson had sixteen pairs of stows somewhere on Treak Cliff. Each pair is a wooden windlass, often a miniature, required by mining law to be set up on each meer. A meer is a length of 32 yards along a vein. Only one is distinguished in the Barmaster's Book as being on the top of the hill so it implies that the rest were on the steep eastern face or perhaps at or near the Old Tor Mine in the Winnats Pass. As Watson had claimed these "for anything and what he could get", meaning, in lead-miners' jargon, anything other than lead, he was possibly making sure of his claims by calling them lead mines even though his target was Blue John.

A year later, in 1766, Henry Watson's partner, John Platt, noted a lease from Lady Mazarine "Dec 2, Lady Mazarine let ye Blue John, Castleton". As Blue John is not lead ore, her ladyship retained the rights to all other minerals, no matter who worked the lead. Lady Mazarine was one of the Eyre family with properties all over the Peak District and this note suggests that she was leasing out mining rights for minerals other than lead and Watson was protecting his rights by virtue of both the lead-mining and ordinary legal systems.

Several of Watson's mines were referred to as "old pipes" indicating that they had been worked previously. Only those noted as "new" were fresh developments. Some of these sixteen mines may have been no more than near-surface trials but others were probably substantial mines. It is unfortunate that neither plans nor detailed locations of Watson's mines are known and none can be definitely identified today, but it seems very likely that he was extracting Blue John from the upper parts of both Treak Cliff and Blue John Cavern.

Henry Watson was not alone in laying claims to parts of Treak Cliff for on December 12th 1767 *"Isaac Eeds and partners gave one dish of ore to free a first taker meer west from Robert Layton's Old Founder on Trake Cliff Old Pipe on the Trake Cliff Top. Arrested at Robt Layton's suit, afterwards agreed and the ground laid out".* It is not known exactly where this might have been, and Robert Layton does not appear anywhere else in the archives. Whether Eeds or Layton were mining Blue John is also unknown but the mention of Trake Cliff Old Pipe suggests they might have been.

In March 1768 three pairs of stows at Walton Hole (= Waterhull) were *"nicked at the request of John Kyrke and William Royse, the owner not known"*. Nicking means that the Barmaster was warning someone that he would take over their unworked mines, and, as that someone did not restart working those mines, he assigned the Waterhull title to John Kirk and William Royse. This was two years before John Kirk (or Kyrke) and Joseph Hall are said to have "discovered" the Blue John Cavern which raises doubts about the accuracy of their story of the discovery. Some 19th century accounts have confused the above Joseph Hall with his namesake who founded the Derby marble works: they may have been relatives but it is unlikely that they were the same person.

Tourist visits to the Blue John Mine were already possible in 1777. William Bray in his book "Sketch of a Tour" wrote of travellers being inveigled into going down but he found it rather dirty and uninteresting.

In May 1783 there was another mining dispute on Treak Cliff. As was the usual lead mining custom, the Barmaster, Robert Howe, was asked to call upon two members of the Barmoot Jury *"to go up George Whittingham's Level and see if Rakecliffside and Old Miller Mines were one and the same"*. The Level referred to is probably the present entrance tunnel to Treak Cliff Cavern and the dispute suggests that the miners in the two mines had broken through into each others workings, possibly somewhere near what is now known as the Witches Cave in Treak Cliff Cavern. The result of the dispute is not recorded but normal practice would suggest some sort of compromise or partnership.

Apart from the mining activities described above, there is an oft-repeated story that Henry Watson made the very first "Derbyshire Spar" vase for Lord Duncannon in 1743, with the stone obtained from a block over which his horse stumbled in the Winnats Pass. There are two questions here: firstly, what is meant by "Derbyshire Spar" as the term has been used variably for Blue John, for other coloured fluorspar, for calcite and for alabaster? So the "first vase" may not have been Blue John. Other old names which add to the confusion are "Derbyshire Drop" and "Johnstone", both applied rather variably to Blue John or other minerals.

Secondly, another version of the story is that the spar block was not found in the Winnats Pass but in Middleton Dale (near Stoney Middleton) and that it was a large stalagmite. This story seems more likely to be correct. Henry Watson's nephew, White Watson, included a sketch of a vase made from a stalagmite in his book "A Delineation of the Strata of Derbyshire" (1811) and stated quite clearly that it was found in Middleton Dale. The vase concerned was in the Whitworth Museum at Darley Dale until World War II but it cannot be located now. Those who saw it in pre-war days said it was made from a stalagmite.

There are two other stories concerning the discovery of Blue John. As noted above, John Kirk and Joseph Hall, two miners working in Waterhull Mine, are said to have "discovered" the Blue John Cavern about 1770, though parts of this mine had been worked as early as 1709. Perhaps Kirk and Hall conveniently "re-discovered" the cavern to have a suitable story for visitors.

Yet other story is that John Platt (1728-1810), architect and marble-worker of Rotherham, is said to have been riding down the Winnats Pass when his horse stumbled on a rock, and looking down, Platt saw this bright blue stone. He took it home and made a pair of salt cellars for his client, the Earl Fitzwilliam. He had designed and supervised much building work for the Earl at Wentworth House, near Rotherham, from 1755 onwards.

Another version of the Platt story is that a servant brought a cart-load of stone from the Winnats Pass to build a rockery at Wentworth and the Castleton mineral agent, Robert Hall, who was on a visit, saw the blue stone and drew Platt's attention to it. Platt then made the salt cellars for the Earl. Either way it is not known exactly when Platt made his salt cellars but it was probably between 1755 and 1765. Platt was closely involved with Henry Watson at the Ashford marble works so he might have come across Blue John there anyway. He became part-owner of the works around 1763 and gradually took over the business transactions whilst Watson did the practical work. Richard Brown, marble worker of Derby, also had an interest in the Ashford works for a few years.

Watson retired about 1776 to look after the stone-turning and fitting part of the trade in Bakewell, where his nephew White Watson took over on Henry's death in 1786.

Thus Blue John was clearly in use and in demand for the great houses at least 5 years before Watson's mines were recorded in 1765, so it seems that it came into use somewhere after Fiennes and Leigh's notes of its occurrence around 1700 and before 1760. For Robert Adam to use it at Kedleston Hall in 1761-2 it must have been an established product, well known in Derbyshire, and probably known throughout the country.

Blue John does not seem to have been known by that name until a brief mention in Platt's papers "1766, Dec 2, Lady Mazarine let ye Blue John". Two years later the name Blew John appears in Boulton's letter of 1768.

As the incomplete records of 1709-1710 mining do not mention Blue John they have no significance regarding its discovery or use as an ornamental stone and it leaves us without any clear response to the questions "when was Blue John discovered?" and "when was Blue John first made into ornaments?" The nearest answers that can be offered are that it was known by 1697, possibly as early as 1671, and first used for ornaments somewhere after 1700 and before 1760, possibly by 1743, and even less certainly by 1709.

**One of a set of four magnificent six-point candelabra
supplied to Saltram House, Plymouth, in 1772**

Prominent amongst the leaders of the industrial revolution was
Matthew Boulton (1728-1809). In partnership with John Fothergill,
Boulton's industrial empire was based at the Soho works in Birmingham where machines pressed out all sorts of metal devices such as
buttons, buckles, tableware and "toys" (meaning ornamental gadgets
of various types) as well as components for larger machines. Most
of the metal was steel, but gold, silver and copper articles were also
manufactured, and Boulton was one of the few people who made
Sheffield Plate outside Sheffield. Later, from 1774, he took on a new
partner, James Watt, and together they were responsible for the
development and installation of many steam-driven pumping
engines for mine drainage, which revolutionized mining practice.

In 1761 Boulton was engaged by his friend Robert Adam, the designer and architect, to produce fittings and objets d'art to the latter's designs for Osterley Park, Syon and Kenwood Houses, near London. The small selection of ormolu produced at this date was said to rival that made by the French (Or comes from the French for gold, and molu from the French for grinding or shaping, so ormolu is gilded brass, bronze or, sometimes, just copper, surrounding a polished stone, marble or ceramic core).

By the later 1760s, both the aristocracy and the newly rich industrialists had entered a phase of building stately homes, many designed or furnished by Robert Adam. Re-building earlier palaces and castles was also in vogue in the more settled times after the Jacobean Revolutions.

The end of the Seven Years War in 1763 led to a flood of French ormolu ornaments coming into Britain where they were eagerly bought by British clients. Boulton saw the business opportunity and set out to produce his own "home-grown" supply of furnishings and ormolu in bulk from about 1767 onwards.

With designs derived from classical Italy and Greece as well as some of his own and some "borrowed" from the continent he prepared pattern books of hundreds of different outlines for vases, candelabra, censers and cassolets (perfume jars), clocks and other articles. These could be chosen and ordered by his customers with a choice of the coloured stone or marble in the core framed or adorned by gilded brass. Amongst his favourite core stones was Blue John and many examples made in the late 1760s and in the 1770s can be seen in our stately homes today. Amongst the earliest ormolu with Blue John was a candelabrum said to have been made for Lord Dundas about 1761. Production in earnest did not commence until a few years later.

The ormolu part of his business made little profit and was subsidized by his main manufactory of steel household articles, silverware and Sheffield plate for which he employed 600-700 men. Boulton's pattern books and much of his correspondence survives and have been the subject of several books and articles by Sir Nicholas Goodison.

By 1768 Matthew Boulton wanted as much Blue John as he could get. He tried through an intermediary either to buy the mines of Blue John at Castleton or to lease them for at least a year. The intermediary was John Whitehurst, clockmaker and pioneer geologist, who was a fellow member of the influential Lunar Society. Other members of this Society included Josiah Wedgwood, Joseph Priestley and James Keir (pioneer chemists), Erasmus Darwin (medicine and natural history) and John Baskerville (printer). These and other members were mostly innovative industrialists with mutual interests in publicizing each others products.

Boulton's 1768 letter to Whitehurst survives:

"The principle intention of this letter is to tell you that I have found a new use for Blew John wch will consume some quantity of it. I mean that sort wch is proper for turning into Vases. I therefore would esteem it a singular favr if you would enquire whether the Mine of it has lately been let or when it is to be let again for I wish to take it for a year & if you find that it is not possable to come at it then please to learn how I may come at any of ye best & largest sort of the produce of it but above all I beg you will be quite secret as to my intentions and never let M. Boulton and John Blue be mentioned in ye same sentence. When you come to Soho I will show you what I am about. I am informed that there is one person in Derby that has it, Now if ye mine is not comeatable or if I could not be supply on ye same terms as he is but I had rather have the Mine".

It is uncertain whether Boulton's letter led to purchase or lease of the mines: accounts differ, some said he was unsuccessful but others cite Boulton's own claim to have leased the mines for £1000. However, in 1769 he bought 14 tons of the best quality Blue John from John Platt at £5-15-6 per ton. Platt took over much of Henry Watson's marble business at Ashford-in-the-Water and may have thereby gained an interest in the mines on Treak Cliff registered to Watson in the Barmaster's Book four years earlier. This quantity of 14 tons may well have been the greater part of a year's produce

then. About the same time Boulton bought quantities of Blue John from the mineral agents Robert Howe and Robert Bradbury, as well as vase bodies from "the Widow Hall" (the Hall family were related to Richard Brown, marble worker of Derby, of whom more later). Hatterel, presumably for plinths, was obtained from John Noel at Bradwell.

Boulton employed 35 "chasers" at his Soho works in Birmingham: the term chaser would normally refer only to metal workers but may have included stone turners too. However, their main task was fitting the gilt metal round the stone cores. Numerous coloured marbles were used but Boulton's favourite seems to have been Blue John. Various designs of ormolu were based on classical Roman or Greek objects or with oriental motifs. Clients could order Caryatid, Sphinx, Persian, Venus or other designs as illustrated in his pattern books.

A separate question is how the Blue John was transported to Birmingham. Accounts differ: some say that the Blue John was turned and polished at Castleton to specified shapes and sizes. Robert Bradbury was sent quite specific instructions, often with drawings, of the vases or corestones needed. Other accounts say that the rough stone was shipped and then turned and finished at the Soho works in Birmingham before gilding. In fact, both stories may be right and both rough and prepared Blue John were sent in different consignments. The Blue John items were apparently carried in barrels packed in sawdust as was the usual practice for shipping

A pair of cassolets, part of a chimney garniture set supplied to Queen Charlotte in 1771, now in Windsor Castle

china ware. Preparation done at Castleton was more economical as it reduced the weight to be carried. The barrels had a maximum weight of about 100 lbs and were either carried two at a time on mule back or were shipped in wagons. At least one order was for only two barrels which would not need a wagon.

The transportation of 14 tons as noted above would have required either a long string of mules (probably about twelve per ton) or perhaps three or four wagons and the journey would have taken at least a week.

By 1770 Boulton's ormolu manufactury was sufficiently well known to attract royal attention. King George III ordered a pair of perfume burners for Windsor Castle (jars with perforated gilt lids in which pot-pourri of dried

Blue John turret clock with Wedgwood medallion, photographed in Hopton Hall, near Wirksworth (present whereabouts not known)

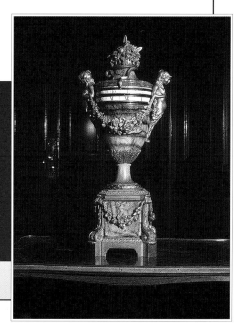

Above left: Blue John &
Ormolu vase, Lauriston
Castle, Edinburgh

Above right: Blue John &
Ormolu vase (present
whereabouts not known)

Right: Blue John &
Ormolu turret clock,
photographed at Hopton
Hall, near Wirksworth

petals gently smouldered to give off scented smoke). This order was quickly followed by an order for a chimney garniture (i.e. a mantelpiece set) for Queen Charlotte in 1770. The design was by Sir William Chambers, the King's architect. The set consisted of two candelabra, two censers (perfume jars) and a clock which are still at Windsor Castle. Another clock with a Blue John backing to the dial was made for the King and is in Buckingham Palace. It has Blue John panels for the sides, all set in an ornate ormolu frame.

Boulton and his partner Fothergill produced many hundreds of ormolu vases and candelabra with coloured marble or stone cores. It is not known how many had Blue John but several dozen articles survive. Notable examples are in Birmingham Museums, Chatsworth House, Saltram House near Plymouth, the Fitzwilliam Museum in Cambridge, and in Warwick Castle. Most items were supplied to order, but from 1771 to 1778 Boulton held annual auction sales at Christie's in London. A variety of vases, urns, candlesticks, candelabra, essence pots, altars, sugar dishes, clocks and figure groups were offered. Typical prices for candelabra were £30-£40 each. Many did not reach their reserve prices and some were unsold. Boulton does not seem to have made much, if any, profit from his ormolu.

Several items at one of Boulton's sales were bought for the Empress Catherine of Russia and were sent to the Imperial Palace in St Petersberg.

Amongst the notable examples of ormolu with Blue John are several elaborate turret clocks. These had the mechanism inside the cup with a Blue John and/or gilt lid. The time was indicated by a snake's head pointer projecting downwards over a moving band with numbers for the hours and small marks for the minutes. Examples are in the Fitzwilliam Museum at Cambridge and in Kedleston Hall, near Derby. Many of the clock mechanisms were French movements but others were made by Boulton's friend Whitehurst at Derby or by Thomas Wright of London.

A pair of Boulton's Blue John and ormolu candelabra were presented by the then Princess Elizabeth to the President of the United States during her visit to Washington in 1951. They are still in the White House.

There is a long-standing story that Blue John was sent to France to be gilded by the ormolu manufacturers there, but no documentary evidence of such export has been found. Some articles have French ormolu fittings but it is possible that the latter were imported and applied in England. The ormolu of the candelabrum and vases in the Wallace Collection in London is not Boulton's work and almost certainly French workmanship dated to the early part of Louis XVI's reign.

There is little doubt that Matthew Boulton's ormolu and Robert Adam's designs for fireplaces in the 1760s and 1770s put Blue John in the forefront of public interest and much of the later craft has depended on their pioneer efforts.

The famous architect and designer Robert Adam is among the first people known to have used Blue John in an item to which a definite date can be assigned. In 1760 he designed fireplaces for Lord Scarsdale at Kedleston Hall near Derby. One of these includes a Blue John plaque. It was made and installed in 1761 by Joseph Hall, marble mason of Derby, whose business was taken over by his brother-in-law Richard Brown. Most other fireplaces can be attributed to Brown & Son's marble works, which were operated by three successive Richard Browns. Doubtless some of the same craftsmen were employed by both Hall and the Browns.

Fireplaces including Blue John all date from the 1760-1780 period. They fall into three design patterns: Blue John panels or plaques; Blue John in long series or rows of small panels, and the long strips called stringing; and Blue John in floral or foliage inlays. About a dozen have been traced though doubtless many more were made and have been destroyed or lost since the 18th century.

The bridal suite in the Friary Hotel in Derby has a Blue John plaque in the silhouette shape of a Grecian urn inset into a white marble fireplace. It can be dated to about 1760.

The finest Kedleston Hall fireplace is of white Carrara marble. It has an oval plaque of Blue John centred below the mantelpiece, composed of six wedge-shaped pieces cut to give continuous blue banding, with an oval piece in the centre cut across the grain (sometimes called dice spar). Side panels of yellow Siena marble have floral mouldings attached. Another fireplace has a frieze of Millers Vein surrounding the grate. Both were designed by Robert Adam about 1760 and installed by Joseph Hall.

Erasmus Darwin's House, at 3 Full St. Derby, had a fine fireplace with three Blue John panels, the centre-piece being several slabs fitted to show continuous banding, and much stringing with Blue John strips in different sizes. It was designed by the architect Joseph Pickford, carved by George Moneypenny and installed by Richard Brown in 1782. The house has long been demolished and the fireplace was sold to a dealer. Fireplaces with Blue John panels were also installed at two other Darwin residences near Derby, Breadsall Priory and Sydnope Hall, but neither are there now.

Meynell Langley Hall has a white marble fireplace with a rectangular Blue John panel in the centre with a white moulded relief figure fastened to it. On either side beneath the mantelpiece are stylized inlays of urns with foliage including "leaves" of inlaid Blue John. The date is uncertain but it probably dates from around 1780.

A diocesan retreat near Derby has a white marble fireplace with an alabaster mantelshelf and a strip of yellow Siena marble. The panel beneath the mantelpiece has one large and two small oval

Left: Fireplace in the Georgian House, Bristol, panelled with Millers vein

Below: Fireplace with a Blue John centre panel and with Blue John obelisks on the mantle piece, Kedleston Hall, near Derby, installed 1761

Above left: Fireplace in Alscott House, near Stratford-on-Avon

Above right: Blue John panels set in the reredos at Stapleford Park Church, near Melton Mowbray in 1784

Below: Fireplace said to have once been in Sydnope Hall, near Derby

Blue John plaques with stringing between. The side panels are ornamented with stylized foliage of Blue John inlaid into white marble. Restoration of the Blue John inlays was carried out about 1990.

Long Eaton Hall, now the Council offices, has a small fireplace with Blue John stringing to Joseph Pickford's design, installed in 1778. Most of the fireplace is a mottled yellow Siena marble. Blue John stringing is in the side panels inlaid into white marble. A rectangular centre panel is of Blue John with a large oval relief mount of a reclining figure stuck to it.

Pickford's own house in Friargate, Derby, now part of Derby Museums, has a fireplace with Blue John panels installed about 1769-70. The Blue John occurs as stringing on either side of a mottled marble centre panel. A thin band of Blue John occurs in two marble urns moulded at either side.

Thurgarton Hall, between Nottingham and Southwell, has a partly white and partly yellow marble fireplace with matched inlaid groups of stylized foliage containing Blue John on either side of a white moulded marble centrepiece.

Alscott Park House, near Stratford-upon-Avon, has a fine white marble fireplace with a Blue John panel over a metre long made of slabs of Millers Vein fitted together beneath the mantelpiece as well as side panels.

The Georgian House, part of Bristol Museums, has a fine fireplace with the grate surrounded by a frieze of Blue John. A block of Millers Vein has been cut to give the appearance of continuous banding.

Staunton Harold house on the Derbyshire/Leicestershire border, now a Cheshire home, has a white marble fireplace in its shop containing a single rather pale rectangular panel of Blue John in the centre with coloured marble on each side.

Parwich Hall, near Ashbourne, has a mottled white marble fireplace with Blue John panels inset in the top and both sides.

Abington Manor Museum, Northampton, has a white marble fireplace with Blue John stringing installed in about 1770.

Although not a fireplace, another important piece of Richard Brown & Son's work may be noted here. It is the reredos behind the altar in Stapleford Park church near Melton Mowbray, Leicestershire. Installed in 1784 it has nearly eighty small Blue John panels inlaid into white marble along the top and an archway made of eleven larger panels beneath.

Gilt bronze & Blue John candelabra made by Matthew Boulton

Leaving aside the grand items of Adam style fireplaces and Boulton's ormolu, Blue John was made into a large variety of smaller items in the late 18th and 19th centuries. As with the fireplaces, Brown & Son in Derby were leading manufacturers until 1864 when Joseph & Thomas Hall took over, using steam power for sawing and turning marble and Blue John. Blue John was made into vases, chalices, urns, candlesticks, jars, salt cellars, perfume jars, pomanders, spill-jars, sugar bowls, finger bowls, columns, obelisks, paperweights, ash-trays, ink-stands, watch-stands, pen racks, book ends, knife-handles, button-hook handles, eggs, door knobs and, of course, jewellery. The latter included rings, ear-rings, brooches, pendants, necklaces, bracelets, cuff-links, tie-pins, hat-pins and, occasionally, buttons. In addition, Blue John was widely used as an inlaying material in Ashford Black Marble ornaments. As noted in the "Discovery" section of this book, Henry Watson and later John Platt were also among the principal workers of both marble and Blue John. Henry's nephew White Watson (1760-1835) carried on the business and dealt in Blue John up to 1835. He also tutored the 6th Duke of Devonshire in mineralogy.

*Above: Blue John vases
and columns
(H. H. Harrison Collection)*

*Opposite; Top: A selection of
Blue John Jewellery*

*Bottom: Blue John
Kedleston Vase*

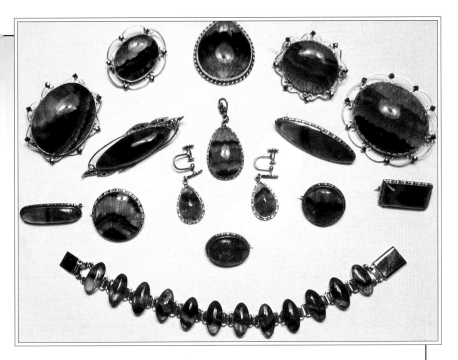

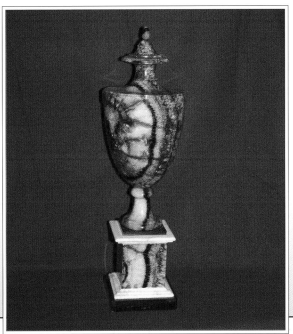

Amongst late 18th century uses for Blue John, two items stand out. They are the inlaid frieze in a white marble memorial plaque in St Helen's Church, Darley Dale, dated 1775. About the same time the risers of the Grand Staircase in Chatsworth House were panelled with Blue John; regrettably this staircase was later replaced with a different design without Blue John.

On the whole the larger 18th century articles were solid and less delicate suggesting to some investigators that resining was unknown. John Mawe's book "Mineralogy of Derbyshire" (1802) gave quite a detailed description of working Blue John without mentioning resining at all. This omission contrasts with Boulton's workers having treated Blue John with it 30 years earlier, and antique vases brought in for repair have clearly been resined. Resining was sometimes regarded as a trade secret and some craftsmen would never talk about it even as recently as the 1950s.

Whilst many of the articles in the late 18th century were made in Castleton, others were turned and polished in Buxton, Ashford-in-the-Water, Bakewell, Matlock and Derby. Some articles produced in these places were probably marketed through Brown & Son in Derby and through Boulton in Birmingham. Little record has survived but Boulton's successor James Campbell was listed as "a manufacturer of Derbyshire spar" until his death in Birmingham in 1820.

The early 19th century brought in hollow items such as deep bowls and vases in a great variety of shapes. Most of these show increased translucency as they had been resined, though when it was applied a little too enthusiastically the Blue John took on a yellow hue.

Tourism increased at the very end of the 18th century with the opening of such attractions as the Speedwell Mine at Castleton. Though Peak Cavern was not involved in Blue John mining, there were workshops adjacent to its approach with shops attached to attract tourists visiting this Wonder of the Peak. The Blue John Cavern was improved for tourists from 1836 onwards and had both workshop and shop outside. The early 19th century saw several

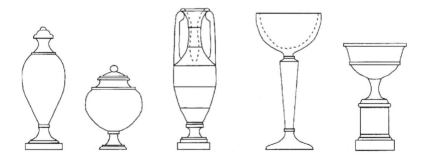

18th century vase designs possibly by Boulton but without ormolu.
(further examples on page 81)

A page from Matthew Boulton's pattern books showing designs of vases which could be supplied with Blue John cores in the ormolu fittings

Blue John vases
(H. H. Harrison Collection)

**A pair of Blue John goblets,
Kedleston Hall, Derby**

William Adam's Royal Museum (with the bay window) at Matlock Bath, c. 1840

"grottos" opened at Matlock Bath and several shops selling marble, spar and Blue John ornaments appeared along The Parade.

The development of Smedley's hydropathic establishment at Matlock brought in floods of visitors and the arrival of the railways in the 1860s increased the flood to a torrent. "Petrifactioneers" had shops selling fossils, mineral specimens, marble (particularly the inlaid Ashford Black Marble) and, of course, Blue John. Several of the shops styled themselves "Museums", literally places where one could muse whilst making up one's mind to purchase something. The petrifactioneers were sometimes known as "baublers" and their products were baubles.

Whilst much was made of Derbyshire marble at the Great Exhibition of 1851, there was remarkably little mention of Blue John. At best there are listings of "marble and spar ornaments", where "spar" apparently included alabaster, Blue John and Crich fluorspar.

Buxton was another centre for the tourist trade. Its warm springs had attracted many visitors from the 16th century and the improvement of access to Poole's Cavern in the 1850s boosted trade in various Derbyshire products such as fossils and minerals, as well as marble and Blue John.

The petrifactioneers' establishments in Matlock and Buxton became the leaders in the field, competing to make the most attractive items and displays. Amongst the leading petrifactioneers were Mawe, Shore, Adam and Vallance in Matlock, and Woodruff and Noel in Buxton. The Derby marble and spar works of Brown & Co continued activity and was later taken over by J. & T. Hall. Regrettably very few items are signed or can be attributed to any particular maker. Occasionally labels may be found stuck under the base. It is worth a look at the craftsmen's backgrounds as they were fascinating people in their own right.

John Mawe (1766-1829) had several years at sea as a teenage seaman during which he collected shells and minerals in many parts of the world. On his return he started work with Brown & Son in Derby in 1793, later becoming manager of their shop in London. He became a partner after marrying Richard Brown II's daughter a year later. As a result of his marble work he became interested in geology and spent several summers learning the lay-out of the Peak District's strata. Later, in 1807-

1811, he was commissioned by Portuguese royalty to make a mineral collection in Brazil and he travelled widely in South America. In 1811 he returned to England and opened shops in Matlock, Castleton, Cheltenham, Scarborough and London. He published several books including the "Mineralogy of Derbyshire" (1802) which included the earliest known diagram of Treak Cliff and its Blue John mines. A later book was "Familiar Lessons in Geology" (1821). He spent some weeks in Castleton each autumn and bought up much Blue John for use in his workshops there and at Matlock. Mawe's shop at Castleton was managed by Mr Needham who later bought it and ran it for 50 years. Mawe took on Vallance as an assistant and later William Adam came from Cheltenham to join Mawe. On the latter's death in 1829 first Vallance and later Adam assisted Mawe's widow before setting out on their own. Mawe's widow became Mineralogist to the Queen and had a shop in the Strand, which was later sold to the noted mineral dealer James Tennant. Blue John was among the stock in trade in all the Mawe shops and his assistants Vallance

and Adam soon became familiar with it.

Little is known of **James Shore** except that he claimed to have made the largest Blue John vase in 1815. It was 24 inches (60 cm) high, including the plinth, and was made of a series of rings fitted one above the other using Blue John from the Bull Beef Vein. Shore sold it to Mawe and on his death it passed into William Adam's hands and remained a centre-piece of his shop/museum. It was illustrated in Adam's book "Gem of the Peak" 3rd and 4th editions with a curious change in the upper section and handles suggesting that it had been damaged and rebuilt. The engravings suggest that it had Blue John handles. The contents of Adam's shop were sold by auction in 1849 and the vase eventually passed into the Chatsworth Estate hands. At the Great Exhibition of 1851 a very large Blue John vase was shown by W.Jepson of Edensor, who was the lessee of the Edensor Inn. Contemporary reports suggest that the vase was Jepson's own work but this seems very unlikely. The vase is still in Chatsworth House, where it now has black marble handles and a much lower plinth. However, Shore's 1815 vase is not the largest Blue John vase ever made - see below.

John Vallance (1781-1853) started as an assistant to Mawe at the Old Royal Museum but later set up on his own at the Centre Museum - next door! Vallance made what is probably the largest Blue John vase ever made. As with Shore's it was built up out of a series of rings but using stone from the Five Vein, with double scroll handles in Blue John. It was 31 inches (80 cm) high, seven inches more than Shore's, and was made about 1842. Vallance's vase is almost certainly that presented by S.Addington in 1868 to the Geological Museum, now part of the Natural History Museum in South Kensington. Vallance had a shop in London as well as Matlock. He won a gold medal for his marble ornaments at the Great Exhibition but if he showed any large Blue John vases there little was made of them. He died only two years later.

Thomas Walker (died 1872) took over Vallance's establishment in 1853, calling it the Royal Centre Museum, possibly combining the two adjacent museums for a time. The Museum was later operated by Mr Dakin and then by Herbert Buxton who exhibited an uncut block of Blue John weighing more than a quarter of a ton outside his shop for many years before it was sold to the Natural History Museum for £100. The Royal Museum later came into the hands of William & Samuel Smith.

William Adam (1794?-1873) came to Matlock as an assistant in Mawe's business; later he helped the latter's widow before taking over the Old Royal Museum in his own right (the building now known as the Royal Museum is next door - formerly Vallance's Centre Museum). Adam offered his services in arranging or supplying collections of fossils and minerals, and gave lectures on minerals and related topics. He, too, made several large Blue John vases. The Duke of Devonshire became William Adam's patron and he made the largest one-piece Blue John tazza for the Duke. With the bowl 20 inches in diameter it is on display in Chatsworth House today. William Adam boosted his business by writing several books on the Peak District. His "Gem of the Peak", which went to six editions 1838-1857, has an appendix on minerals in which he claimed to be the first to use floral inlays in Black Marble, though stylized foliage had been used in Robert Adam's (no relation) fireplaces 80 years before. William Adam also introduced the idea of the Romans having used Blue John in the "Gem of the Peak", doubtless as a sales gimmick. In spite of William Adam

boosting his sales with stories of Roman origins, large Blue John vases, fine inlaid marble and several books, his business failed and the contents of his shop had to be auctioned in 1849.

Several other large vases survive at Chatsworth House, Kedleston Hall, the Natural History Museum and elsewhere. Doubtless Mawe, Vallance and Adam made some of these but there are no signatures or documentation. A Grecian urn style vase at Renishaw Hall (the home of the Sitwell family near Sheffield) is 22 inches (55 cm) high and $14^{1}/_{2}$ inches in diameter but nothing is known of its maker or history, but it is very like the Shore

A fine Blue John bowl in Lauriston Castle, Edinburgh

1873. CASTLETON.

VISITORS TO CASTLETON ARE INVITED TO CALL AND INSPECT

JOHN TYM'S

COLLECTION OF

BLUE-JOHN ORNAMENTS,

Derbyshire Ware, Fluor Spar, Minerals, Fossils, Ferns, Polished Specimens, &c.

Trays and Cabinets of

DERBYSHIRE MINERALS.

Great Variety at Reasonable Prices.

Trays and Cabinets of Fossils from the Mountain Limestone; Fossils from all British Strata; Cheap Elementary Collections of Fossils; Minerals, and Rocks, specially arranged to illustrate Lyell, Page, and other geological hand-books with or without cabinets); Portfolios of Dried Mosses and Ferns (forming elegant Drawing Room books), suitable for presents.

CATALOGUES POST FREE.

Postal Address—JOHN TYM, Castleton, near Sheffield, (and at the Speedwell Cavern, foot of the Winnats.) *1875*

John Tym's advertisement for Blue John ornaments, 1873 - 1875

vase now in Chatsworth House. A fine pair of bell-shaped vases 21 inches high and 12 inches in diameter are also in Chatsworth House.

Thomas Woodruff (c.1820-1904) started his business in Bakewell in 1842. In 1851 his inlaid tables designed by L.W. Gruner won a gold medal at the Great Exhibition. One table was purchased by Prince Albert, who commisioned Woodruff to carry out speciality works at Osborne House on the Isle of Wight. By 1856 Woodruff found it more profitable to move to Buxton, initially with a show room in The Quadrant, later in the Colonnade. He was a skilled inlayer and his

"Grapes Table", now in Buxton Museum, is the prime example of the art: he used Blue John for the ripe and yellow Siena marble for the unripe grapes. It was shown at the 1862 Exhibition at which Woodruff won a medal, though it is not recorded whether this particular table was the prize-winner. He also made a magnificent "ormolu" table of Blue John, which was exhibited in the Thermal Baths building during the visit of Princess Mary in 1921. Woodruff's business was later taken over by his partner E. White and the table was in his shop in 1924. A few years later it was sold to Charles Boot at Thornbridge Hall, Great Longstone. When the contents of that house were sold in 1946 it was bought by Arthur Ollerenshaw Sr. and is now in that family's Cavendish Museum at Castleton. It is just over 3 feet in diameter with a circular top made of triangular slices of the Millers Vein arranged on a sector pattern: it is mounted on a gilded cast iron frame of ormolu style.

Joseph Noel (active 1846-1876) and his family were skilled spar and marble workers and had a spar museum. His workshop and shop have been reconstructed in Buxton Museum. An earlier Noel was noted in 1784 as employing his son aged 8 and his daughter aged 9 as "skilled turners".

Selim Bright (active 1856-1884) had another marble and spar shop in the Crescent at Buxton. He too exhibited at the Great Exhibition and gained an Honorable Mention.

William Arden (active c.1850-1900) had a shop in Buxton Market Place and produced both fine inlay work and Blue John ornaments.

The Black Marble works at Ashford used Blue John but it seems to have been more of a sideline after Watson's and Platt's interests. Apart from inlay work with Blue John they apparently made various "spar" ornaments and these probably included Blue John, though it is not usually mentioned separately. Brown & Son (and Mawe for a time) operated the works 1818-1833 when **George Oldfield** took over until 1853. Oldfield also exhibited at the Great Exhibition. He had a showroom adjacent to the main Bakewell-Buxton road. **Joseph Twigg & Co** ran the works from 1853 to 1899 and it closed in 1905. **George Redfern** ran a separate marble works in Ashford from 1846 to 1881. He too made "spar" ornaments. Amongst other Black Marble and spar workers in Ashford were several members of the **Tomlinson** family. Their inlaying workshop was the last to close in 1905, and a descendant, J. M. Tomlinson, has compiled the definitive history of Derbyshire Black Marble (1996).

Joseph & Thomas Hall, great-grandsons of the Derby marble works founder in 1760 Joseph Hall, and successors to Richard Brown, operated the works there 1864-1876. Their manager **Robert Lomas** then took over and continued until the 1920s. Lomas used Blue John in several places, in particular the reredos at Mackworth Church, near Derby, with its intricate design of Blue John and other coloured stones inlaid into alabaster (1878). Lomas also set Blue John panels into alabaster communion balustrades in 1893. He advertized Blue John as suitable for ecclesiastical work in 1895. Whether Halls or Lomas were involved in making the inlaid marble work in the Albert Chapel at Windsor Castle is not known, but the Blue John thistle and flower heads suggest that they may have been. Lomas also made an egg-shaped Blue John lamp shade but it is not known whether this survives.

Whilst Castleton was the source of Blue John, it did not really come on to the tourist map until the very end of the 18th century, though Peak Cavern had long been open to visitors. The Speedwell Mine began to attract them as soon as

**The large Shore vase in
Chatsworth House**

Above: The largest Blue John vase, made about 1842 by John Vallance, now in the Natural History Museum, London

Right: A contemporary sketch of Vallance's giant vase, with a different neck and handles

the boats were available in the 1780s. Neither Peak nor Speedwell Caverns had any direct connection with Blue John working but their shops offered Blue John items for sale. The Blue John Cavern was open to visitors from around 1777 but access to the lower caverns was by climbing down a miners' ladder of stemples and few went down until access was improved by Micah Tym about 1836. Castleton was primarily a lead-mining village with Blue John mining and working as a secondary industry. Henry Watson claimed lead mining rights in 1765 though it had been mined actively for years beforehand. He and his partner Platt leased the rights to the Blue John deposits in 1766 from Lady Mazarine (nee Eyre; the Eyre family had extensive interests in lead mining in the Castleton area) but they were later sold to the Champion family of Edale. **Jeremy Royse (1741-1829)** was their agent for Blue John mining from 1790 until his death. He was followed by his son **Samuel Royse (1791-1871)** who died only a few months before his son **Joseph Royse (1814-1871)**. The significance of a note in the Barmaster's book for 1856 that Samuel Royse bought the Miller Mine from a Mrs Royse is uncertain as he was the Champions' agent for all the mines throughout the mid 19th century. After Samuel Royse and his son Joseph died a few months apart in 1871, William Champion leased the whole of Treak Cliff to John Lowe and Henry Eyre in partnership. They employed **Walter Royse (c.1820-1892)** as overseer until 1892, when his son, **John Royse (1876-1945)**, took over the tenancy. The output of Blue John was limited to three tons per annum. Later, in 1919, William Champion sold the Blue John Cavern to Charles Markham for £1500, though another note says that Mrs V.H. Eyre of the Nags Head was the proprietress in 1891. The rest of the hill was also sold in 1919 to Colonel John Broadbent.

The Royse family had several branches involved in mining around Castleton and legend has it that one family member was born in the Speedwell Mine where his mother was sorting lead ore! John Royse opened Treak Cliff Cavern to the public in 1935.

The Royses were registered agents or lessees of four separate mines through most of the 19th century:

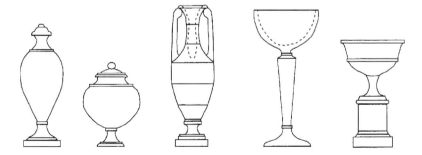

1. Cliffside;
2. Millers Pipe;
3. Old Tor;
4. Waterhull Pipe.

All four were registered for both lead ore and for coloured fluorspars. Cliffside and Millers Pipes are now merged into Treak Cliff Cavern. Waterhull Pipe is part of the Blue John Cavern. The Old Tor Mine is on National Trust property high in the Winnats Pass. Access is not normally allowed.

As is usual today, the operators and guides in the caverns spent much of the winter months mining and turning Blue John when there were few visitors around. Amongst the guides was **John Tym** (1830-1902) who helped his father there from about 1850. Later he leased the Speedwell Cavern and he had a spar museum opposite the Castle Hotel (now the Information Centre). One of the best craftsmen, John Tym made a Blue John window of 250 pieces set in a frame like a church's stained glass window, 6 feet high and 3 feet wide. On appointment to the Curator's post at Stockport Museum in 1895 he took the window

with him and it is still on view there. Other Blue John windows are in Chatsworth House (81 pieces each about 6 inches square of alternating Blue John and stalagmite), Buxton and Manchester Museums but there is no record of who made them. Apart from Royse's and Tym's activities there were several other spar museums in Castleton, operated by the Needham, Eyre and Hall families. Mawe's Museum was managed and later bought by **Thomas Needham** who ran it for a total of 50 years. Hall's Museum was on the approach to Peak Cavern.

The above marble and spar workers in Castleton, Matlock, Bakewell, Ashford, Buxton and Derby were the leading entrepeneurs dealing in Blue John. Directories list 30 spar and marble workers in Derbyshire in 1829 (with 150 workmen in total), 13 in Buxton alone in 1846 were reduced to 9 in 1864. They were turning out a steady flow of Blue John vases, chalices, urns, candlesticks, bowls, obelisks, and jewellery. Many examples can be seen in stately homes large and small. Few can be attributed to any particular worker and even fewer can be dated.

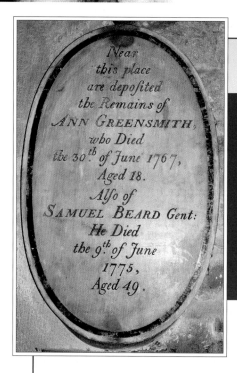

Near
this place
are deposited
the Remains of
ANN GREENSMITH,
who Died
the 30th of June 1767,
Aged 18.
Also of
SAMUEL BEARD Gent:
He Died
the 9th of June
1775,
Aged 49.

Left: Memorial plaque with a Blue John border in St Helen's Church at Darley Dale

Below left: James Shore's vase as it appears in Adam's "Gem of the Peak" 3rd edition 1843 (compare with the photo on page 86)

Below right: As it appears in the 4th edition 1848

THE LARGEST
BLUE FLUOR SPAR OR
BLUE JOHN VASE
IN THE WORLD.
MADE IN 1815.

After the poor showing of Blue John at the Great Exhibition of 1851, there were only limited appearances at other comparable industrial arts exhibitions in 1855, 1862, 1870, 1882 and 1884 and their catalogues sometimes spoke of the declining trade. By the early years of the 20th century there was little Blue John mining and working. The spar museum/shops in Buxton and the works in Derby had closed and the Ashford Black Marble works closed in 1905. Only one shop kept going in Matlock and is still with us today. A dealer in minerals in Matlock, J.Greatorex, carried a stock of rough Blue John and decided to sell it by auction in 1913. Blocks weighing about one hundredweight (roughly 50 kgs) were sold for only £1.15s.0d and £1.7s.6d respectively. Smaller pieces made only $5^1/_2$ d to 8d per pound.

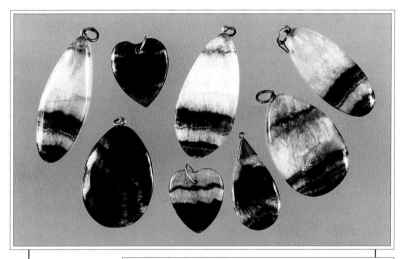

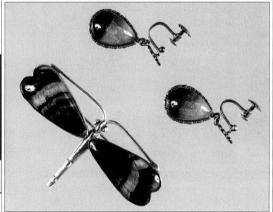

Above: Blue John Pendants

Right: Blue John Dragonfly brooch and ear-rings

With the moribund state of the Blue John trade up to and during World War I it was not surprising that the landowner, Mr William Champion of Edale, decided to sell the whole property in 1919. It was effectively split into two lots and sold by auction. The Blue John Cavern was sold to Sir Charles Markham who is reputed to have used it as a sort of playground for rich friends before selling it again in 1924 to Arthur Ollerenshaw. The latter had already taken over the Speedwell Mine as a tourist attraction in 1921 so with both that and the Blue John Cavern he had two thirds of the cave tourist trade together with the main outlet shops. He had a workshop at the cavern entrance. The Blue John Cavern has remained with the Ollerenshaw family ever since, but the Speedwell Mine was sold to his relations, the F.W. & H.Harrison partnership in 1940. They later established a workshop at the cavern entrance.

The rest of Treak Cliff, together with the non-lead mineral rights, was bought in 1919 by Colonel J.Broadbent, M.P. for Ashton-un-der-Lyne. Percy J. Turner already had a 5 year lease of fluorspar and baryte rights and added to these by "nicking" the lead-mining rights. Under the old lead mining laws any mine could be nicked, i.e. claimed if a mine was not being worked for lead ore to the satisfaction of the Barmaster. Even so very little lead ore was ever produced. The nett result of nicking the lead rights and a lease of non-lead minerals from Col. Broadbent was that Percy J. Turner sublet the lease to G.T.

West & Co of Liverpool who re-opened the combined Miller and Cliffside Mines both for industrial fluorspar, then in demand as a flux for the iron and steel industry, and for Blue John, which was sold to several craftsmen.

G.T.West & Co constructed an inclined railway for lowering wagons of fluorspar from the old quarries above what is now Treak Cliff Cavern down to a loading bay on the roadside. Fluorspar was also brought out of the present exit tunnel and loaded on to the railway nearby. More was brought out of the entrance tunnel and tipped down a chute behind the present shop. West & Co advertized good quality Blue John for the ornamental trade but the poorer material went for metallurgical purposes and was tipped into blast furnaces. Some fluorspar, including Blue John, is even reputed to have been exported to America. Some good quality Blue John was quietly hidden by the local miners and retrieved later! Two lorry loads of good quality Blue John were sent to Grant's marble and spar works near Torquay, who supplied Blue John ornaments to various customers for many years afterwards. West & Co's operations lasted for about ten years.

During G.T.West & Co's operations in 1921 the miners broke into a small cave with human remains - a late Neolithic burial site from about 3000-3500 B.C. – the sight of a skull is said to have caused consternation amongst the miners! Five years later, in 1926, the miners broke into another range of caverns –

this time they were liberally decorated with stalactites, though the caverns had no new Blue John veins. Almost immediately West & Co. had the idea of opening up the new caverns to the public but their lease was due to run out in four years so the discovery was kept quiet. In 1929 they attempted to renew the lease, using the Sheffield cave explorer, J.W. Puttrell, as agent, but they were apparently unsuccessful.

A few years after West & Co's operations had ceased, in 1934, Col. Broadbent leased the combined Cliffside and Miller Mines and the new caverns to the same John Royse who had been mine agent for William Champion earlier. He developed paths and lighting and opened them to the public at Easter 1935 under the name "Wonder Caves". This was spelled out by lines of white-painted rocks on the hillside, and later reduced to just "Caves"; both were visible from half a mile away. After World War II the name was allowed to lapse and they became known as **Treak Cliff Cavern**. John Royse retired in 1945 and died soon afterwards, the last of a dynasty of Royses connected with Castleton mining. Treak Cliff Cavern was then leased by Mrs Broadbent to the Harold Harrison Partnership in 1945. Subsequently the partnership bought the lease from Mrs Broadbent's daughter, Mrs Connery, and they still operate it today. They also established a workshop at the cavern entrance.

The opening of Treak Cliff Cavern in 1935 gave a boost to public interest in Blue John and the workshops at the three

caverns, together with associated shops in Castleton village, have maintained a steady flow of Blue John products ever since. These include small vases, bowls, urns, jars, boxes, knives with Blue John handles, paperweights, ashtrays, cigarette boxes, stone eggs and jewellery, such as rings, brooches, tie-pins and pendants.

John Walker was lessee of Peak Cavern from the Duchy of Lancaster for most of the 1930-1950 period. Whilst that cavern has no direct connection with Blue John mining, Walker had a workshop and shop where the Ollerenshaw's Cavendish Museum is today and he made some fine Blue John ornaments. One piece is notable - a Blue John font still in Castleton's Methodist Chapel. It is a miniature of the usual font, being only about 9 inches high. Another smaller version was made for Sparrowpit Chapel.

Almost all Blue John working was done by treadle lathes until around 1950 when electric motors became generally available and their use is universal today. Electric drills are used for mining in place of hand-driven drills and wedges.

During 1942-43, as part of the war effort, the Ministry of Supply arranged for Czech refugees to extract fluorspar from the top of Treak Cliff by opencast methods. This was largely poor quality Blue John and to judge from the size of the pits no great quantity was ever produced. The Czechs also sank a shaft and had a short inclined railway near Odin Mine, and drove an adit into Odin Gulley, all with only a small output.

Above: Onyx ashtray, clock & cigarette box
with Blue John trim inlay

Below: Lightweight Blue John vases
(H. H. Harrison Collection)

After Col. Broadbent's death in 1947 his widow decided to donate the greater part of Treak Cliff, together with Mam Tor, to the National Trust. The gift excluded the caverns and their mineral rights which remain in the hands of the present operators. The gift, however, included the Winnats Pass and the Old Tor Mine so that part of the Blue John deposits and mine-workings is the National Trust's property today. Unofficial mining for Blue John in the Old Tor Mine in the 1970s was taken by the Court to constitute theft and that mine has since been closed by order of H.M.Inspector of Mines.

The present operators of the Blue John and Treak Cliff Caverns have long had a policy of not selling raw Blue John outside Castleton, so that the few shops still selling it in Matlock etc are working on old stocks.

The majority of the Blue John articles made in the 20th century have been small, mainly jewellery, but a few notable pieces have emerged from the workshops. Several Blue John windows have been made. The finest is in Stockport Museum. Other win-dows are in the Ollerenshaw's Cavendish Museum in Castleton, and in Manchester Museum. A fine example is in Chatsworth House, though not normally on view to the public. Another small window was in Birchfield House at Hope but has since been moved to Buxton Museum.

Several special pieces of Blue John have been made for royal occasions. A fine Blue John chalice was made by W. & S. Smith in Matlock to mark the visit of Queen Mary in December 1913. In 1960 their descendant, Arthur Smith, made a bracelet and a pair of ear-drops for Princess Marga-ret on the occasion of her wedding to Antony Armstrong-Jones (later Lord Snowdon) together with cuff-links for her husband. John Walker in Castleton is said to have made a tobacco jar for the Duke of Kent on his wedding in 1934. Another fine chalice was made by Robert and David Harrison as a Silver Jubilee present for Queen Elizabeth in 1977. The then Princess Elizabeth presented a pair of Blue John and ormolu candelabra to President Eisen-hower during her visit to Washington in 1951.

Extensive collections of Blue John articles can be found in the cavern shops in Castleton.

The **Cavendish Museum**, Castleton, has some magnificent vases, but the item to see is the Blue John table made by Thomas Woodruff in Buxton around 1860.

Castleton Gift Shop has a good collection of vases and bowls and some unusual ornaments, such as a "Mushroom on a Rock" carved out of Blue John.

Chatsworth House, near Bakewell, (Duke of Devonshire) has the largest one-piece Blue John tazza ever made, plus a variety of other vases and ornaments. A Blue John window has 81 pieces of Blue John alternating with slabs of banded stalagmite each about 15 cm square. The window and what is believed to be Shore's "largest" vase of 1815 are not normally on public view.

Kedleston Hall, near Derby (National Trust) has Blue John fireplaces, inlaid tables and several ornaments.

Windsor Castle has the ormolu fireplace garniture made by Boulton for Queen Charlotte about 1770. It is normally kept in Her Majesty's private quarters and is not on public view. The Albert Chapel (adjacent to St George's Chapel) has extensive panelling in various marbles with Blue John used for the flower heads of Scottish thistles and for bosses.

Buckingham Palace has Matthew Boulton's "King's Clock" and other ormolu items.

Buxton Museum has the Grapes Table with Blue John used for the ripe grapes together with Italian marbles for unripe grapes and leaves inlaid into Ashford Black Marble, made by Thomas Woodruff about 1860. There are several other Blue John vases and other ornaments.

Sheffield City Museum (Weston Park) has a fine collection of vases and bowls though, unfortunately, it is what is left of a much larger collection bequeathed by J.W. Puttrell in 1939, much of which was destroyed or damaged by bombing in World War II. Part of Puttrell's collection came from Erasmus Darwin's former home at Breadsall Priory near Derby, which is now a hotel-cum-country club.

Stockport Museum (Vernon Park) has the finest Blue John window ever made. It was brought from his home in Castleton by their former Curator, John Tym, in 1895. There are several other vases etc.

Manchester Museum has a Blue John window and several nice vases.

Birmingham City Museums have an important collection of Matthew Boulton's ormolu vases etc. as well as a variety of other ornaments without ormolu. Some articles are kept in their Elizabethan property at Aston Hall and others in Boulton's home at Soho House.

Derby Museum has a collection of vases. Their 18th century Pickford's House has a Blue John panelled fireplace and a variety of ornaments, including an unusual pair of ormolu-trimmed obelisks.

Exeter Museum has a collection of vases, notably the bells vase, with ten small Blue John bells hanging round the lip of a tazza.

Leicester City Museum has a small collection of vases, some normally on display in their Belgrave House property.

The Natural History Museum, South Kensington, has the largest Blue John vase thought to have been made by J.Vallance of Matlock about 1840. There is also one of the largest bell-shaped vases ever made. There are several smaller articles and some fine display specimens including a "double stone" nearly 1 metre long.

Anglesey Abbey, near Cambridge, (National Trust) has a variety of vases and pillars etc.

Lauriston Castle, (a property in the care of Edinburgh City Museums) has a magnificent collection of 75 vases, urns, tazzas and bowls of many shapes. The collection was built up by the previous owners 1900-1928.

Manderston House, Duns, Berwickshire (Lord Palmer) has many Blue John items, mainly fireplace garnitures, some with ormolu.

The Georgian House (part of Bristol City Museums) has a fireplace panelled with Blue John of the Millers Vein.

Saltram House, Plymouth, (National Trust) has a collection including four six-branched ormolu candelabrum.

The Wallace Collection, London, has a fine Boulton ormolu candelabra.

The Fitzwilliam Museum, Cambridge, has an ormolu turret clock.

St Helen's Church, Darley Dale, near Matlock, has a memorial plaque with a Blue John surround inlaid into white marble.

All Saints Church, Mackworth, Derby, has some unusual Blue John inlay work in the alabaster reredos as well as Blue John panels set in alabaster altar rails.

Stapleford Park Church, near Melton Mowbray, has a frieze of Blue John panels and an archway made of larger panels in the reredos. Made by Brown & Son of Derby about 1784.

Alscott Park House, near Stratford-upon-Avon, has a fine Blue John panelled fireplace as well as a variety of other ornaments.

A small collection of Blue John vases etc is in **Downe House,** Charles Darwin's home in Kent.

Many other stately homes have just one or two vases, some of them ormolu. Several other civic or county museums have one or two articles.

Opposite: Blue John flowers inlaid in the reredos, Mackworth Church

Above: Woodruff's Blue John table – now in the Cavendish Museum, Castleton

Blue John has been used in a variety of ecclesiastical settings.

Two tombstones in Castleton churchyard have small slabs inlaid.

A Blue John panel surmounted by a crucifix was set into the Sheffield City Battalion Memorial in Sheffield Cathedral in 1919.

Hemispherical bosses about 3 inches in diameter are attached to an ornamental fountain in the square of Torrington, north Devon.

Bosses and thistle heads in low relief are inlaid into elaborate marble panelling in the Albert Chapel of Windsor Castle.

Blue John was inlaid as part of the decoration of the pulpit in All Soul's R.C. Church in Peterborough about 1912, but has since been removed.

A memorial plaque in St Helen's Church as Darley Dale, near Matlock, has an oval frieze of Blue John strips.

The chapel of Stapleford Park Church, near Melton Mowbray, has a white marble reredos inlaid with some 80 Blue John panels.

Mackworth Church, near Derby, has much alabaster work, some inlaid with panels, foliage or spiral strips of Blue John.

A miniature Blue John font, only 9 inches high, is in Castleton Methodist chapel.

The altar cross at Hope Church has small Blue John bosses set in the brass.

The Blue John windows at Stockport, Manchester and Buxton Museums and at Chatsworth have already been mentioned, as has the ormolu-type table in the Cavendish Museum at Castleton.

A few lamp shades or bowls have been made from Blue John. The only ones known today are in private possession in Castleton. A Blue John lamp bowl was advertized by R.G.Lomas in Derby around 1920 but its whereabouts are unknown.

A medicinal use for ground-up Blue John was indicated by the following letter sent from Mr Greaves, a former resident of Bakewell, who had settled in Halifax, Nova Scotia. He wrote to George Gould of Bakewell in July 1799 asking for *"four or six pounds of blue fluorspar as I use it in powder for the gravel with great success"*. In this medical context gravel meant gall stones and Mr Greaves evidently drank a concoction with powdered Blue John in it. White Watson sent a consignment to Mr Greaves in September 1799 and another in 1802.

There is a long list of publications dealing with Blue John. Only those with something significant regarding the geology, mineralogy, use and history of Blue John are listed below. Readers who wish to study any particular theme are referred to these and to the further references listed therein.

Adam, W. 1851. **Gem of the Peak**. 5th edition, Mozley, Derby, 405pp. (reprinted by Moorland, Hartington, with a biographical introduction by T.D.Ford, 1973).

Blount, B. & Sequira, J.A. 1919. Blue John and other forms of fluorite. **Journal of the Chemical Society**, vol. 115, pages 705-709.

Braithwaite, R.S.W., Flowers, W.T., Haszeldine, R.S. & Russell, M. 1973. The cause of the colour of Blue John and other purple fluorites. **Mineralogical Magazine**, vol. 39, pages 401-411.

Dunham., K.C. 1952. **Fluorspar**. Geological Survey Special Reports on Mineral Resources. vol. 4, 4th edition. 143pp.

Ford, T.D. 1955. Blue John fluorspar. **Proceedings of the Yorkshire Geological Society**, vol. 30, pp. 35-60.

Ford, T.D. 1969. The Blue John deposits of Treak Cliff in relation to the Boulder Bed. **Proceedings of the Yorkshire Geological Society**, vol.37, pp.153-157.

Ford, T.D. 1992. **Treak Cliff Cavern and the Story of Blue John Stone**. Published by Harrison, Taylor & Co. Castleton. 24pp.

Ford, T.D. 1992. The largest Blue John vases ever made. **Peak District Mines Historical Society Bulletin**, vol. 11, no.5, pp.264-266; also no.6, p. 282.

Ford, T.D. 1996. **The Castleton area**. Geologists Association Guide Book no. 56. 94pp.

Ford, T.D. & Quirk, D.G. 1995. Mineralization of the South Pennines. **Geology Today**, vol. 11, no.5, pp. 172-177.

Ford, T.D. & Rieuwerts, J.H. 1983. **Lead Mining in the Peak District**. Peak Park Publication, Bakewell. 160pp.

Continued on page 104...

*Blue John panels in the
altar rail, Mackworth
Church, near Derby*

Left: The Blue John window in Chatsworth House

Below: Blue John font in Castleton Methodist Chapel

Ford, T.D., Sarjeant, W.A.S. & Smith, M.E. 1996. The Minerals of the Peak District. **Peak District Mines Historical Society Bulletin**, vol. 12, no.1, pp.16-56.

Galwey, A.K., Jones, K.A., Reed, R. & Dollimore, D. 1979. The blue coloration in banded fluorite (Blue John) from Castleton, Derbyshire. **Mineralogical Magazine**, vol.43, pp.243-250.

Goodison, N. 1974. **Ormolu - the work of Matthew Boulton**. Phaidon Press, London. 398pp.

Howie, R.A., Pegram, E. & Walsh, J.N. 1982. The content of rare earth elements in English fluorites: a preliminary study. **Journal of the Russell Society**, vol. 1, no.1. pp.22-25.

Hughes, G.B. 1953. Derbyshire Blue John. **Country Life**, Dec.3rd. pp. 1834-1839.

Lowental, A.I., Harden, D.B. & Bromehead, C.E.N. 1949. Vasa Murrhina. **Journal of Roman Studies**, vol. 39, pp. 31-37.

Mackenzie, K.J.D. & Green, J.M. 1971. The cause of the colouration in Derbyshire Blue John and other blue banded fluorites. **Mineralogical Magazine**, vol.38, pp.459-470.

Mawe, J. 1802. **Mineralogy of Derbyshire**. Published by Phillips, London. 211pp.

Mueller, G. 1954. **The distribution of the coloured varieties of fluorites in the thermal zones of the Derbyshire mineral deposits**. 19th International Geological Congress, Algiers, Comptes Rendus, Fasc. 15, pp.523-539.

Ollerenshaw, A.E. (c.1960). **The story of the Blue John Cavern and Mine**. Published by the author, Castleton. 24pp.

Ollerenshaw, A.E. (c.1960). **The history of Blue John stone**. Published by the author, Castleton. 24pp.

Rieuwerts, J.H. 1996. An abortive early 18th century trial seeking lead ore in the Blue John Mine and Cavern, Castleton. **Technical Speleological Group Journal** (Castleton), no.15, pp.5-13.

Royse, J. 1943. **Ancient Castleton Caves.** Published by the author, Castleton. 2nd edition 1944, 76pp.

Tomlinson, J.M. 1996. **Derbyshire Black Marble.** Peak District Mines Historical Society, Special Publication No 4. Matlock. 96pp.

Tunmer, E.J.E. 1942. Blue John working. **Transactions of the Hunter Archaeological Society,** vol.5, pp. 232-241.

Tunmer, E.J.E. c.1942. **Blue John.** Private Publication, Hathersage, Sheffield. 12pp.

ACKNOWLEDGMENTS

Thanks are due to the Royal Collections Enterprises at Windsor Castle, the Chatsworth Settlement Trust, the National Trust, and to the Natural History Museum at South Kensington, and the Derby, Sheffield, Stockport, Manchester, Buxton, Exeter and Birmingham Museums and Lauriston Castle, Edinburgh, for supplying photographs or giving permission to photograph the Blue John articles in their care. The Central Photographic Unit of Leicester University helped with close-up photography. Thanks are due to Peter Harrison, Bob King, Jim Rieuwerts, Evelyn Dixon, Lindsey Porter and Wes Taylor for reading various drafts and making constructive suggestions.

THE AUTHOR

Biographical Note about the Author: T.D.Ford, O.B.E., Ph.D., B.Sc., F.G.S.

Trevor Ford was brought up in Sheffield and gained his degrees there before becoming Lecturer in Geology at the University of Leicester. He spent 38 years on the staff rising to become Senior Lecturer and Associate Dean of Science. His research interests have been mainly on the Peak District's geology, minerals, mines and caves, as well as on Precambrian fossils and the geology of the Grand Canyon, with some 320 publications on these topics. He was Honorary Editor of **Cave Science** for over 30 years, and has been Hon Editor of **Mining History** for the last 35 years. He was awarded the O.B.E. in 1997 for services to geology and to cave science.

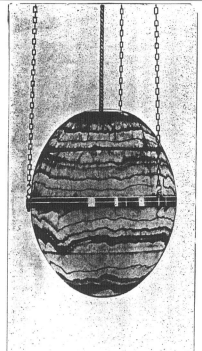

Bowl of Blue John.

R. G. Lomas & Sons

41, King Street, DERBY,

Opposite page; Top: Blue John eggs, Puttrell Collection

Bottom: Blue John lamp bowl advertized by R. G. Lomas in Derby about 1921

Above: John Tym's Blue John window in Stockport Museum

Fireplace with Blue John panel and foliage, Meynell Langley

Above: Blue John panel in a fireplace believed to have been in Erasmus Darwin's House

Below: Fireplace at Thurgarton Hall

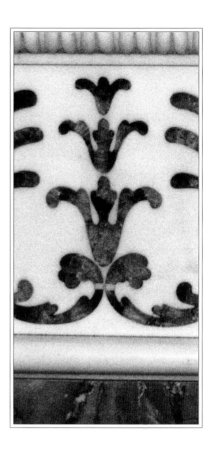

Left: A Blue John Window at Buxton Museum. Purchased with assistance from the Museum & Galleries Purchase Grant Fund

Above: Detail of the fireplace at Thurgarton Hall (see p.109)

Dovedale & the
Manifold Valley
ISBN: 1-873775-15-6
152 historic photos
96pp, £5.99p

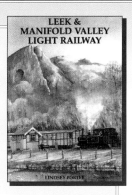

Leek & the Manifold
Valley Light Railway
ISBN: 1-874-723-82-6
138 historic photos
96pp, £3.99p

Peak District
Secrets & Curiosities
*Volume 1: Home & Village Life
Churches & Chapels*
ISBN: 1-873775-17-2
64pp, £3.95p

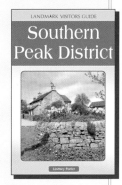

Landmark Visitors Guide:
Southern Peak District
ISBN: 1-901522-27-X
96pp, £4.95p

Ashbourne
Shrovetide Football
ISBN: 1-873775-14-8
Over 200 photos
112pp, £5.99p

Colourful
Peak District
ISBN: 1-873775-18-0
128pp, £5.99p

**To order send a cheque/Visa/
MasterCard details to:**

Ashbourne Editions
Waterloo House, 12 Compton, Ashbourne,
Derbyshire DE6 IDA England
Tel: 01335 347349 Fax: 01335 347303
e-mail: landmark@clara.net

Produced by
Landmark Publishing Ltd,
Waterloo House, 12 Compton, Ashbourne
Derbyshire DE6 1DA England
Tel: 01335 347349 Fax: 01335 347303 e-mail: landmark@clara.net

For the Publishers
Ashbourne Editions
12 Compton, Ashbourne, Derbyshire
Tel: 01335 347349 Fax: 01335 347303 e-mail: landmark@clara.net

1st Edition
ISBN 1-873775-19-9

© Trevor D. Ford 2000

British Library Cataloguing in Publication Data: a catalogue record
for this book is available from the British Library.

Print: Gutenburg Press, Malta
Designed by James Allsopp
Cover design by Samantha Witham & James Allsopp

Front cover: Blue John Tazza, Chatsworth House
Back cover: Blue John vases in Lauriston Castle, Edinburgh

Picture Credits

Chatsworth Settlement Trust: Cover
Leslie Steeples, Buxton Museum: p2
Exeter City Museum: p3
Supplied by the National Trust: p58, p66BL, p78T & p86TL
Supplied by gracious permission of Her Majesty the Queen: p65 & p73
Bristol City Museum: p66TL
Thomas Coulbourn & Sons, Sutton Coldfield: p67 & p109T
Peter Harrison: p38 & p83B
Birmingham Central Library: p77
Derbyshire County Council: p110
All other pictures are supplied by the author